Genstat 5
An Introduction

Genstat 5
An Introduction

PETER LANE

Rothamsted Experimental Station, Harpenden

NICK GALWEY

Department of Applied Biology, University of Cambridge

and

NORMAN ALVEY

CLARENDON PRESS · OXFORD

1987

Oxford University Press, Walton Street, Oxford OX2 6DP

Oxford New York Toronto
Delhi Bombay Calcutta Madras Karachi
Petaling Jaya Singapore Hong Kong Tokyo
Nairobi Dar es Salaam Cape Town
Melbourne Auckland
and associated companies in
Beirut Berlin Ibadan Nicosia

Oxford is a trade mark of Oxford University Press

Published in the United States
by Oxford University Press, New York

British Library Cataloguing in Publication Data
Lane, Peter, 1952–
Genstat 5: an introduction.—Rev ed.
1. Genstat (Computer system)
I. Title II. Galwey, Nick III. Alvey,
Norman IV. Alvey, Norman. Introduction
to Genstat
519.5'028'553 QA276.4
ISBN 0-19-852209-6
ISBN 0-19-852214-2 Pbk

Library of Congress Cataloging in Publication Data
(data available)

Set by Computerised Typesetting Services, Finchley
Printed in Great Britain by
St Edmundsbury Press,
Bury St Edmunds, Suffolk

Preface
Do you need Genstat?

Genstat is a general statistical program designed to help people summarize and analyse information with computers. Computers can save time and trouble, yet telling a computer what to do can be a troublesome business in itself. The many general-purpose computing languages, such as Algol, Basic, Fortran and Pascal, are designed to deal with the details of arithmetic and communication between a person and a computer; but quite ordinary methods of analysis require long programs. Testing and correcting your own programs involves a lot of work. So specialist 'packages' of programs have been developed which require only a few instructions to do standard analyses; but, if you want something different, you will find it difficult or even impossible to modify the instructions.

Genstat gives you the best of both worlds: the flexibility of a programming language with almost the simplicity of operation of a package. It provides this through a statistical programming language, allowing you to specify standard analyses with few instructions, and to construct your own analyses simply and concisely. Programs are very much shorter than the equivalent in a general-purpose language, and so mistakes are fewer and easier to find and correct when they occur.

Here are some of the things that Genstat can do.

a) Plot graphs — histograms, scatter diagrams, lines and contour maps.

b) Form tabular summaries of information.

c) Assess relationships between variables by means of regression analysis.

d) Estimate differences between groups by means of analysis of variance.

e) Identify patterns in data by means of multivariate analysis.

f) Model the behaviour of series of observations by means of time-series analysis.

These techniques are useful in agronomy, animal husbandry, genetics, ecology, medical research and other areas of biology, as well as in industrial research and quality control, economic and social surveys; in fact in any field of research, business or teaching where statistics are used. If you need to interpret information in any of these ways then read on.

The version of Genstat described here is called Genstat 5 Release 1. New versions will appear, adding new techniques and facilities, and will be called Release 2, Release 3 and so on: the contents of this book will still be relevant to these, though some of the detail of the results produced by Genstat may change. Previous releases of Genstat, numbered 4.04, 4.03 and so on, used a different language, described in the book *An introduction to Genstat* (Alvey, Galwey & Lane, 1982, Academic Press, London).

Genstat is available on many types of computer, ranging from microcomputers like the IBM XT personal computer, through mini computers like the VAX 11/750, up to mainframe computers like the ICL 2900. Genstat is constructed with the widely available programming language Fortran 77, and can potentially be used on any type of computer with a compiler for this language and enough storage space. If Genstat is not mounted on the computer you want to use, then contact the distributors of Genstat:

> Numerical Algorithms Group
> 256 Banbury Road
> Oxford OX2 6NN England

This book explains how to use Genstat for some of the commoner statistical tasks. The information you need in order to tell Genstat to do these tasks is introduced throughout the book in the context of practical examples. We suggest you read through the book without skipping any sections, except possibly Section 7.3, as an understanding of one chapter depends on material described in earlier chapters. There are exercises at the end of each chapter to encourage you to practise writing Genstat programs: the best way to learn about any programming language is to write programs and try them out on a computer. Solutions to all the exercises are provided in the Appendix.

After reading this book you may want to find out how to do other statistical tasks with Genstat. The companion book *Genstat 5: a second course* (Digby, Galwey & Lane, 1988, Oxford University Press) describes many of the standard tasks not covered by this book, as well as showing how to write general programs for non-standard tasks. The *Genstat 5 reference manual* (Payne, Lane *et al*, 1987, Oxford University Press) describes all the facilities in Genstat in full.

Harpenden and Cambridge   P. W. L.
March 1987   N. W. G.
                                                                         N. G. A.

Acknowledgements

We are grateful for permission to use material published in the book *An introduction to Genstat* (Alvey, Galwey & Lane, 1982, Academic Press Inc. (London) Ltd). That book was about a previous version of Genstat, called Release 4.04, which had a different command language.

We would like to thank all the friends and colleagues who have helped us to prepare this book.

CONTENTS

1 Basic operations: 'Reading, writing, and arithmetic'

1.1 Introduction

To use a computer to perform calculations on a set of data you need to discover how to do two things. Firstly you have to compose instructions, in a language that the computer understands, to get the data into the computer, carry out the required calculations and print the results for you to look at. In this chapter we shall consider how such a set of instructions, called a program, is constructed using the *Genstat language*. Secondly you have to get the instructions into the computer and tell it what language you have used. This second step will be discussed in Chapter 2.

Genstat is a large computer program designed to help you to analyse data. You give instructions to Genstat by writing smaller programs in the Genstat language which allows you to specify what you want concisely. You can then concentrate on the broad plan of an analysis and Genstat will take care of the details that must be communicated to the computer.

In the following chapters you will see various types of calculation that can be done using the Genstat language: these are standard statistical methods of summarizing and analysing data. But in this chapter we shall start by showing you how to 'read and write' in Genstat and how to do some simple arithmetic. The arithmetic in the first example can be done quite easily with a small calculator, or even in your head. Neither computers nor Genstat are normally used for such simple problems, but the simplicity of the example will leave you free to concentrate on the elements of the Genstat language, which will be built on in later chapters.

We shall use an example close to the hearts of householders in cold climates who are often concerned about the amount of energy required to heat their homes. As the cost of energy increases, it becomes more cost-effective to pay for various methods of insulation to avoid wastefully heating the air outside the house. One such method is the double-glazing of windows.

1.2 A simple Genstat program

1.2.1 Getting the data in: 'Reading'

The numbers below are data from a semi-detached house in south-east England. The dimensions of each window in the house are recorded together with the temperature of the corresponding room, averaged over the heating season (1st October to 1st May for this house).

Width (m)	Height (m)	Average room temperature (°C)
0.39	0.55	17.1
1.05	1.18	17.1
2.40	1.96	16.6
2.06	1.26	16.6
0.48	0.90	14.5
0.56	0.96	14.5
1.06	0.98	16.2
1.54	0.96	14.5
1.04	0.96	14.5
2.02	0.92	15.0

A set of data of this kind is sometimes referred to as a *data matrix*, because it is laid out in an array with rows (corresponding here to windows) and columns (corresponding to measurements). People use statistics in many applications and they may have other jargon words to describe a data matrix; for example, in collections of crop varieties rows are known as 'accessions' and columns as 'descriptors'. Other general words for rows are plots, units, individuals, subjects, cases and observations; and for columns there are variables, variates, factors, attributes, characteristics and measurements.

Calculations in all applications are usually done with whole columns of numbers, while each row is treated in the same way as any other. For this reason the Genstat language is designed to refer to individual columns and to store the numbers in each column together. To work out the amount of money that could be saved by fitting double-glazing to each window, we shall construct a sequence of instructions in the Genstat language, called a *Genstat program*. The three columns of data will be needed in the program, as well as three further numbers (the average outdoor temperature, the change in rate of heat-loss due to fitting double-glazing, and the cost of heat) which will be given later. Therefore one of the first instructions in the program is a statement of the names that we shall use to identify these columns. In addition it is necessary to say what type of data are to be stored and how long the columns are. The following Genstat *statement* contains all this information:

```
VARIATE [NVALUES=10] Width,Height,Roomtemp
```

The meanings of the various parts of this statement are as follows.

The *directive name* VARIATE means that the statement sets up some *data structures* of a type called *variates*. A variate can store a series of numbers. There are other types of data structures in Genstat but variates are the most commonly used because most people deal with series of numbers.

The *option* [NVALUES=10] means that the Number of VALUES in each variate will be 10: this is sometimes called the *length* of the variate.

The *parameter* Width,Height,Roomtemp consists of the names of the three variates to be declared. Names of data structures are formally known as *identifiers*. They can consist of up to eight letters or digits but the first character must be a letter. (In fact the percentage sign (%) and the underline character (—) are also treated as letters in Genstat.)

A Genstat program consists of a sequence of statements like this VARIATE statement. While each statement has a different meaning, they all have a similar form, namely:

directive name [options] parameters

To keep clear the distinction between these parts of a statement, we shall write the directive name and option names in capitals and use a leading capital followed by lower case letters for all identifiers. In fact for directive and option names either case is accepted. For identifiers, case is important: for example, the identifier A is different from the identifier a. Both could be used in the same program to name different structures, though it might not be wise to do so.

Before doing any calculations about the windows we must get the data into the data structures. This is done by a READ statement:

```
READ Width,Height,Roomtemp
```

This is an instruction to read values for the three variates, presented in the same way as in the table above; that is, in the order:

width of first window,
height of first window,
temperature of room containing first window,
width of second window, and so on.

After the READ statement come the values themselves:

```
0.39   0.55   17.1
1.05   1.18   17.1
2.40   1.96   16.6
2.06   1.26   16.6
0.48   0.90   14.5
```

```
0.56   0.96   14.5
1.06   0.98   16.2
1.54   0.96   14.5
1.04   0.96   14.5
2.02   0.92   15.0 :
```

You will see later, in Chapter 2, Section 2.4, that data values can be read from elsewhere if you wish.

The data values are in *free format*: that is, each value is distinguished from the next by a separator. Here the separator is one or more spaces or new lines: this is the easiest and most commonly used form for recording data. But if you have data already prepared in some other order or in some other format, this can be specified too as you will see later (Chapter 4, Section 4.3.1 and Chapter 8, Section 8.2.1). The colon marks the end of the data, and Genstat will check the number of values up to the colon against the number that has been declared in the VARIATE statement. Clearly there is not much problem with only 30 values, but when hundreds of values are to be read it is essential to know that they have been assembled correctly.

1.2.2 Simple arithmetic

The data are now available for use in the calculations. The rate of heat-loss through a window is the product of its area, the temperature difference across the glass and the thermal conductivity. To start with, we can work out the area of each window from its height and width. There will be 10 of these areas, so a new data structure is set up to hold them:

```
VARIATE [NVALUES=10] Area
```

A straightforward statement suffices to do the simple arithmetic needed to give values to the new structure:

```
CALCULATE Area = Width * Height
```

The asterisk (*) stands for 'times' and tells Genstat to multiply corresponding values of Width and Height. The symbol = tells Genstat to store the resulting sequence of numbers in the variate Area. It is therefore known as the *assignment operator* rather than by its more common name of 'equals'. This distinction (common to most programming languages) is not a mere quibble. For example, the statement

```
CALCULATE B = B + 2
```

which appears to be mathematical nonsense, is valid in Genstat. It means: 'Take the values of the structure labelled B, add 2 to each of them and put the resulting values in the structure labelled B.' The old values of B are therefore lost; but this may not matter and the storage space that would be occupied by a new structure has been saved.

The next calculation involves the average temperature difference across the glass during the part of the year when the house is heated. The data include the average room temperatures during this season but the average outside temperature must be obtained from a published table (*Energy in the home workbook*, 1978, Open University Press, Milton Keynes): 5.7°C is the relevant figure for the house in this example. This value can be assigned in the program to a data structure called a *scalar*, which holds a single number:

```
SCALAR [VALUE=5.7] Airtemp
```

We also need to know the change in thermal conductivity, or 'U-value', when a window is double-glazed. The manufacturer of one common system states that his value is 2.0 W/m²/°C for a house in a sheltered situation, so this number is put in a second scalar:

```
SCALAR [VALUE=2.0] Uchange
```

The change in the rate of heat-loss through each window can now be calculated and stored in a further variate called Rchange:

```
VARIATE [NVALUES=10] Rchange
CALCULATE Rchange = (Roomtemp − Airtemp) * Area * Uchange
```

The figures we are really interested in are the costs of the heat wasted through each window, so the rates must be multiplied by the length of the heating season and the cost of the heat. Another published table (also from the *Energy in the home workbook*) states that there are 18.4 million seconds between the first of October and the first of May. At present the cost of heating (in megajoules, MJ) is £0.0051/MJ, after adjusting for the efficiency of the gas boiler in the house. Using this information the cash savings in pounds can be worked out with a CALCULATE statement:

```
VARIATE [NVALUES=10] Cashsave
CALCULATE Cashsave = Rchange * 18.4 * 0.0051
```

Notice that the actual numbers are included in this CALCULATE statement. There is a choice in Genstat between doing this and using a scalar structure: the latter is used in practice when the number itself has to be calculated from the data, or is needed repeatedly.

1.2.3 Displaying the results: 'Writing'

Having calculated the results, we want to look at them: there is no point in the computer knowing the answer if it is not instructed to tell us. The PRINT statement is provided for this purpose, and states what values to print and in what form they should appear:

```
PRINT Area,Cashsave
```

The values of each variate will be laid out automatically in a column, headed by the identifier of the data structure. The numbers will be printed using a sensible format, such that the mean of each variate would appear with four numerically significant digits.

The end of the program is marked by a STOP statement; therefore the complete program is as follows:

```
VARIATE [NVALUES=10] Width,Height,Roomtemp
READ Width,Height,Roomtemp
0.39   0.55   17.1
1.05   1.18   17.1
2.40   1.96   16.6
2.06   1.26   16.6
0.48   0.90   14.5
0.56   0.96   14.5
1.06   0.98   16.2
1.54   0.96   14.5
1.04   0.96   14.5
2.02   0.92   15.0 :
VARIATE [NVALUES=10] Area
CALCULATE Area = Width * Height
SCALAR [VALUE=5.7] Airtemp
SCALAR [VALUE=2.0] Uchange
VARIATE [NVALUES=10] Rchange
CALCULATE Rchange = (Roomtemp - Airtemp) * Area * Uchange
VARIATE [NVALUES=10] Cashsave
CALCULATE Cashsave = Rchange * 18.4 * 0.0051
PRINT Area, Cashsave
STOP
```

1.3 Running the program

The program can now be presented to the computer, for example by creating a file
containing the statements, and then running Genstat with that file as the input file.
This and other ways of using Genstat are discussed in the next chapter. The printed
results are shown below:

```
Genstat 5  Release 1
Copyright 1987, Lawes Agricultural Trust
(Rothamsted Experimental Station)
   1  VARIATE[NVALUES=10]Width,Height,Roomtemp
   2  READ Width,Height,Roomtemp

      Identifier  Minimum    Mean  Maximum  Values  Missing
          Width     0.390   1.260    2.400      10        0
         Height     0.550   1.063    1.960      10        0
       Roomtemp     14.50   15.66    17.10      10        0

  13  VARIATE[NVALUES=10]Area
  14  CALCULATE  Area = Width * Height
  15  SCALAR[VALUE=5.7]Airtemp
  16  SCALAR[VALUE=2.0]Uchange
  17  VARIATE[NVALUES=10]Rchange
  18  CALCULATE  Rchange = (Roomtemp – Airtemp) * Area * Uchange
  19  VARIATE[NVALUES=10]Cashsave
  20  CALCULATE  Cashsave = Rchange * 18.4 * 0.0051
  21  PRINT Area,Cashsave

      Area   Cashsave
     0.214    0.459
     1.239    2.651
     4.704    9.623
     2.596    5.310
     0.432    0.713
     0.538    0.888
     1.039    2.047
     1.478    2.442
     0.998    1.649
     1.858    3.244
  22  STOP
******** End of job. Maximum of 1118 data units used at line 18 (41764
      left)
```

First of all this output shows which version of Genstat is being used: this is Genstat 5 Release 1. There have been many previous releases, as described in the Preface; future releases will be made from time to time, called Release 2, 3 and so on, incorporating new features into the program.

Next a copy of the statements is displayed. Notice that the lines have been automatically numbered for easy reference: the numbers were not with the original statements.

Each statement is executed as it occurs and any printed results will appear immediately below the statement producing them. The READ statement produces a summary of the data (but not a copy of the individual values). The minimum, mean, and maximum values for each variate are shown and also the number of values and whether any are missing. The PRINT statement produces the required values of the window areas and the savings if each window were double-glazed. Finally there is a message about how much storage space in the computer has been used.

Note that the output from the program includes a listing of the program itself but not quite in the form that we wrote it. If you were to copy a program from the output, it would be incomplete because the data values have not been reproduced. Also you must not include the line numbers in your program — these are added by Genstat. In most future examples of output we shall include the listing of the statements that produced the output. But we shall not always give the original form of the complete program as well, so you should bear these differences in mind.

1.4 Controlling the form of printed results

The results of the PRINT statement were laid out by Genstat automatically. The columns of numbers were printed side by side, each number being right-justified in a field-width of 12 characters, and being printed with three decimal places. Also, the columns were headed with the identifiers of the variates. All these aspects of the printing can be modified by setting options or parameters in the PRINT statement. Usually, such modifications are not needed, because Genstat will choose a sensible default setting. But Genstat cannot guess here that the results for Cashsave are amounts of money and so would be best printed to the nearest penny: that is, with only two decimal places. This can be specified by setting the DECIMALS parameter of the PRINT statement:

```
PRINT Area,Cashsave; DECIMALS=3,2
```

This gives the following output:

```
22  PRINTArea,Cashsave;DECIMALS=3,2
       Area   Cashsave
       0.214     0.46
       1.239     2.65
       4.704     9.62
       2.596     5.31
       0.432     0.71
       0.538     0.89
       1.039     2.05
       1.478     2.44
       0.998     1.65
       1.858     3.24
```

In some circumstances it may be more convenient to print information like this in separate columns, one after the other rather than side by side. That type of layout can also be specified, by setting an option of the PRINT statement:

```
PRINT [SERIAL=yes] Area,Cashsave; DECIMALS=3,2
```

The default setting of the option SERIAL is 'no', giving the parallel form already shown when the structures to be printed have the same number of values. The output from the statement above is as follows:

```
23  PRINT[SERIAL=yes]Area,Cashsave;DECIMALS=3,2
       Area
       0.214
       1.239
       4.704
       2.596
       0.432
       0.538
       1.039
       1.478
       0.998
       1.858
    Cashsave
       0.46
       2.65
       9.62
       5.31
       0.71
```

```
0.89
2.05
2.44
1.65
3.24
```

There are several ways in which the program could be shortened. For example, you could combine all the VARIATE statements into a single statement, since they all declare structures of the same length:

```
VARIATE [NVALUES=10] Width,Height,Roomtemp,Area,Rchange,Cashsave
```

Similarly, the scalars could be declared in a single statement:

```
SCALAR Airtemp,Uchange; VALUE=5.7,2.0
```

Notice that SCALAR statements, and others like VARIATE that declare structures and have an option to supply the same values for all structures declared, also have a parameter to supply separate values for each structure.

Finally, you could also make the calculations more compact (see Exercise 1(3)). Other methods of saving time and space will be discussed in Chapter 5.

1.5 Statements, lists, and identifiers

The statements used in this example convey diverse instructions in the same basic form:

directive name [options] parameters

The directive name indicates the general nature of the operations to be performed; for example, CALCULATE or PRINT. Each directive name is a *system word* of the Genstat language, which means that it is associated with a particular kind of operation and that its special significance can be recognized by Genstat.

The options, if any, give more detail about the precise nature of the operations: for example that the variates being declared have 10 values. The setting of an option is usually a single number or identifier, though you will see other types of setting in later chapters. Always, though, the setting of an option is applied to all items that appear in parameters. Thus the statement

```
VARIATE [NVALUES=10] Width,Height,Roomtemp
```

indicate that all three variates are of length 10.

If there is more than one option, they are separated by semicolons (;). All options have an option name, such as NVALUES above, which specifies which option is referred to out of the many possible in some statements. Like directive names, option names are system words.

The parameters usually supply the identifiers of structures to be operated on by a statement. Each parameter setting is usually a *list*, and all parameters have names unless there is only one parameter in the statement. For example, the PRINT statement in the program above could have been written:

```
PRINT STRUCTURE=Area,Cashsave; DECIMALS=3,2
```

but in practice it is natural to omit the name of the first parameter. Parameter names too are system words of the Genstat language.

If the parameter setting is a list with more than one item, the items are separated from each other by commas, and if there is more than one parameter, these are separated by semicolons (;). Thus in the statement

```
SCALAR Airtemp,Uchange; VALUE=5.7,2.0
```

there are two parameters, each a list of two items.

The settings of some parameters are *expressions* rather than lists. An expression is made up of identifiers and numbers, together with round brackets and the operators:

+	plus,
−	minus,
*	times,
/	divided by,
**	to the power of, and
=	is assigned.

For example, there is an expression in the statement:

```
CALCULATE Rchange = (Roomtemp − Airtemp) * Area * Uchange
```

CALCULATE is a statement with only one parameter: the setting is an expression which cannot be named.

Like options, parameters give more detail about the nature of the operations to be performed, but they differ in two important ways from the options. Firstly, all parameters in a statement are treated as parallel; in other words, the numbers or identifiers in each parameter are matched according to the order in each list. For example, in the statement

```
PRINT [SERIAL=yes] Area,Cashsave; DECIMALS=3,2
```

the values of Area are printed with three decimal places and those of Cashsave are printed with two. Secondly, parameter lists will be recycled if necessary so that each list provides one value for each entry in the first parameter. Thus the statement

```
PRINT [SERIAL=yes] Area,Cashsave,Rchange; DECIMALS=3,2
```

would cause Genstat to associate the 3 with both Area and Rchange. In contrast to these rules, the option settings in a statement remain the same for all items in the parameter lists.

In this book, and in most implementations of Genstat, the options are enclosed in square brackets, but you may find that these or some other less common characters are not available on the computer that you use. Each character in a Genstat program corresponds to a numerical code defined by the American Standard Code for Information Interchange (ASCII). If you find you cannot use any of these characters, ask the computer staff about suitable alternatives.

Notice the difference between system words that are defined in the Genstat language, and identifiers that you can make up to suit your needs. The word CALCULATE is recognized by Genstat as defining the operation to be done. But Rchange and Area could be replaced by any other identifiers, such as R and A, throughout the program. The only difference would be in the labelling of the output.

1.6 Summary

Chapter 1 describes a short program in the Genstat language using the basic operations needed in most applications of Genstat.

All statements in Genstat have the common form:

directive name [options] parameters

where the square brackets and the options are omitted if the default settings of options are satisfactory. The directive name of a statement is a system word that is one of a set of words that Genstat recognizes, associated either with types of data structures, with operations on data or with program structure.

The following statements set up structures to hold data which are referred to by identifiers that you can make up to suit your needs:

VARIATE   holds a series of numbers, and
SCALAR   holds a single number.

The VARIATE statement has an NVALUES option to specify how many values are in the series. The SCALAR statement has a VALUE option and a VALUE parameter to specify the number or numbers to be stored.

The following statements operate on data structures:

READ   puts data into structures,
CALCULATE   does arithmetic, and
PRINT   displays data or results.

The SERIAL option of PRINT can be set to 'yes' to get structures printed in series rather than in parallel. The DECIMALS parameter controls the number of decimal places displayed.

The final statement in any program should be:

STOP   finishes the program.

1.7 Exercises

1(1) A series of crop experiments was carried out at 12 sites. The experiments were sown and harvested on different dates which were recorded (as days after 1st January) together with the total rainfall (inches) and number of hours sunshine at each site:

Sowing date	Harvest date	Rainfall	Sunshine
90	218	11.8	587
96	239	12.6	604
87	220	11.3	431
104	247	10.0	522
89	229	2.5	724
91	230	18.7	398
86	227	6.5	473
110	252	11.1	465
107	246	4.3	591
83	218	13.6	421
99	254	30.8	266
88	231	8.9	672

Write a Genstat program to calculate for each experiment the average daily sunshine and the average daily rainfall in centimetres (1 inch = 2.54 cm). Print the two sets of results separately. Then print the results in parallel with a single statement, using separate formats for rainfall and sunshine.

1(2) Write a program to calculate and print the areas of circles of radius 1,2,3,5,7,11,13,17 and 19 cm.

1(3) If the areas of the windows need not be printed, what single statement could be used to replace all the CALCULATE statements in the program shown in Section 1.2.3? Can you then reduce the program to five statements, not counting the data?

2 Running Genstat on a computer

2.1 Introduction

You do not need to know very much about computers to be able to use them to run Genstat. If you are used to computers, you will probably be familiar with the information in Sections 2.2 and 2.3. If not, before you start using a computer there are two questions to which you must find the answers, and which we cannot answer for you:

1) Is Genstat available on the computer?
2) Are you authorized to use the computer?

If you are authorized to use the computer, you will have access to some type of terminal which is connected to it, and will have details of how to start and stop communication. If many people are allowed to use the computer, this usually involves identifying yourself and giving a password; probably you will type information like this on the keyboard of the terminal.

Once you have established communication with a computer that has Genstat, there are two possible methods of operating with Genstat. We suggest you try first the batch method, running some of the examples in this book, and then experiment with the interactive method to see if it suits you better. The Genstat statements are identical for the two methods: it is the way you use the computer that is different.

2.2 The batch method

You need to answer three more questions in order to run a program with the batch method.

3a) How do you tell the computer you want to use Genstat in batch mode?
4) How do you store information, in this case a program, in the computer?
5) How do you look at the results?

The complete answers to these questions are outside the scope of this book, because computers differ so widely. If you cannot answer the questions now, at least you know what to ask.

Information is usually stored in the computer in *files*: you need to know how to set up a file, and to edit and delete it afterwards. Given this knowledge, the answer to question 4 is to set up a file containing the Genstat program you want to run, for example the program developed in the last chapter, or a program you have written in answer to a problem at the end of that chapter.

To tell the computer you want to use Genstat, you must give it a command or a series of commands in the language of the operating system of the computer. It is probably very simple, like this command on a VAX 11/750 with the VMS operating system:

GENSTAT name of input file,name of output file

However, some operating systems may insist on a space rather than a comma between the file names, or may have some other format for conveying the essential information. In any case, any good operating system should help you find out if you type:

```
HELP GENSTAT
```

The second file name in the GENSTAT command should be a new one: Genstat will set up a new file for you, containing the results.

After giving the command to run Genstat, you may have to wait until the command is executed. This depends on how your operating system has been configured. On some systems, the command may be executed within a few seconds, but on others it will be put in a queue and dealt with according to some scheme of priorities. In any case, you will be prompted in some way when the execution is complete. You can then examine the output file at the terminal, perhaps by using the same editor as you used to create or modify the input file, or tell the computer to print it for you to look at later.

Here is an example of a batch session, running a simple Genstat program on a VAX 11/750. The parts that you would type are shown in light type and the computer's responses are in bold type.

```
RETURN
USERNAME: GENSTATINTRO
PASSWORD: ********
Messages
$CREATE SIMPLE.GEN
SCALAR Nsecs
CALCULATE Nsecs = 60 * 60 * 24 * 365.2475
PRINT Nsecs
STOP
```

```
EXIT
$ GENSTAT SIMPLE.GEN,SIMPLE.LIS
$ TYPE SIMPLE.LIS

Genstat 5   Release 1
Copyright 1987, Lawes Agricultural Trust
(Rothamsted Experimental Station)
   1   SCALAR Nsecs
   2   CALCULATE Nsecs = 60 * 60 * 24 * 365.2475
   3   PRINT Nsecs
          Nsecs
      31557384
   4   STOP
******** End of job. Maximum of 862 data units used at line 3 (42020
      left)

$  LOGOUT
```

2.3 The interactive method

You need to answer only one more question to run a program with the interactive method:

3b) How do you tell the computer you want to use Genstat in interactive mode?

The answer will be very similar to the answer to 3a in the last section, provided that your operating system allows Genstat to be run interactively. If so, the command you must give will probably be as simple as this one for the VAX 11/750:

```
GENSTAT
```

After you type this command, the computer will start running Genstat and will display at the terminal the information about what version of Genstat you are using. Then a prompt will be given for the first Genstat statement: the prompt may be a single character, such as >, or perhaps several characters at the left side of the terminal display. When you have typed a statement, and pressed *RETURN* to send it to the computer, Genstat will display any output generated by it: Genstat does not, by default, display a copy of statements when working interactively. Each line you type is executed in turn until finally you type STOP, when Genstat will stop and you can continue with operating-system commands.

Here is how to run the simple program of the last section interactively, again on the VAX 11/750.

RETURN
USERNAME: GENSTATINTRO
PASSWORD: ********
Messages
$ GENSTAT

Genstat 5 Release 1
Copyright 1987, Lawes Agricultural Trust
(Rothamsted Experimental Station)

> SCALAR Nsecs
> CALCULATE Nsecs = 60 * 60 * 24 * 365.2475
> PRINT Nsecs

    Nsecs
31557384

> STOP

******** End of job. Maximum of 862 data units used at line 3 (42020
    left)

$ LOGOUT

2.4 Using files for input and output

So far, the Genstat programs you have seen use only two files on a computer, one for
input (the program) and one for output (the results). If Genstat is run interactively,
the terminal is effectively treated as if it were both the input file and the output file at
the same time. However, we mentioned in the last chapter that you can read data,
with the READ statement, from other places than from within your Genstat program. It can be convenient to keep data separate from programs, and to keep
different sets of data in separate files but still to use them all in a single program.
There is no difficulty in doing this with Genstat. Again, it involves creating and
referring to files on the computer: you can in fact refer to as many files of data, or
even of Genstat statements, as you want within a Genstat job.

Assume that the data on windows from the last chapter are stored in a file on the
computer, called WINDOWS.DAT. To read the data from this file rather than
putting the data with the statements, the program to do the calculations needs one
extra statement, and one option setting in the READ statement:

```
OPEN 'WINDOWS.DAT'; CHANNEL=2
READ [CHANNEL=2] Width,Height,Roomtemp
```

The OPEN statement assigns a reference number, called a *channel number*, to the file of data called WINDOWS.DAT. Genstat is then instructed to read from this file by telling it to look in channel 2. By default, it would look in channel 1, which always refers to the file containing the Genstat statements. You can use several channel numbers for input files: the numbers available on your computer should be included in the information from HELP GENSTAT.

As well as opening files for input, you can open files for output. A common use for this is to keep a record of the statements in an interactive run of Genstat:

```
OPEN 'WINDOWS.REC'; CHANNEL=2; FILETYPE=output
COPY 2
```

The OPEN statement here assigns the output channel number 2 to the file WINDOWS.REC. The list of output channel numbers is independent of the list of input channel numbers, and you must specify which type you are opening by setting the FILETYPE parameter of the OPEN statement. By default, OPEN assumes that a channel number is to be in the input list.

The COPY statement tells Genstat to store a copy of every Genstat statement given subsequently, in the file with output channel number 2. Thus, after finishing using Genstat interactively, you can inspect this file, or print it as a record of what you did.

Results can also be stored in extra output files, using the CHANNEL option of the PRINT statement. For example,

```
OPEN 'WINDOWS.OUT'; CHANNEL=3; FILETYPE=output
PRINT [CHANNEL=3] Area
```

stores the areas of the windows in a file called WINDOWS.OUT.

A further list of channel numbers is used for graphical output intended for graphical terminals or plotters. The details of producing the output are described in Chapter 3, Section 3.4. In fact, only one channel is allowed in this list.

```
OPEN 'GRAPH.GRD'; CHANNEL=1; FILETYPE=graphics
```

After this statement, the commands for high-quality graphs described in Section 3.4 will store, in the file GRAPH.GRD, coded instructions for the graphical device. The coded instructions can then be sent to the device by a command in the language of the operating system.

2.5 Storage space and time

When you start to use Genstat for practical work, rather than just the small problems at the end of chapters in this book, you may find that you need to change the amount of storage space available or the length of time for which your programs are allowed to run. You can see from the output above that by default we were allowed space for 42882 data values, using Genstat on a VAX 11/750. This space is also used for storing the Genstat statements and details of data structures, and for working space when calculations are done. On other computers, the total available may be more or less than this. To change the default, you may be able to modify the command to the computer that tells it to run Genstat. Similarly, there may be time limits on the running of Genstat programs. The details should be available to you in your computer's HELP system: try typing HELP GENSTAT.

2.6 Summary

Genstat can be run in batch or interactive mode. In batch mode, Genstat is controlled by statements in an input file, and produces results in an output file. In interactive mode, Genstat takes statements typed at a terminal and displays results directly at the terminal.

Other files can be used for input or output by assigning them channel numbers in OPEN statements of the form:

OPEN 'filename'; CHANNEL=number; FILETYPE=string

Three distinct sets of channel numbers can be used for files of type input, output and graphics.

There are CHANNEL options in READ and PRINT to allow data to be read from other files and results to be printed to other files.

A statement of the form:

COPY output-channel-number

keeps a copy of your statements in an output file.

2.7 Exercises

2(1) Store the data for rainfall and sunshine in Exercise 1(1) in a file, with a colon to mark the end of the data. In another file, store a program to read the data and print the rainfall in centimetres and the amount of sunshine in days. Run the program in batch mode.

2(2) Run Genstat in interactive mode. Declare a variate to have 10 values, and read the values 1, 2 up to 10 into it. Calculate and print side by side the values, their squares and their cubes.

2(3) Repeat Exercise 2(2), but keep a copy of the statements in an output file and send the results of the PRINT statement to another output file.

3 Picturing the data

3.1 Introduction

In the first chapter you have seen some of the basic features of the Genstat language, and how it can be used to read, print, and perform calculations on data. But most users of Genstat want something more than such everyday operations: they want to summarize and interpret quite large amounts of data by means of statistical analysis. Before embarking on an ambitious analysis it is sensible to have a preliminary look at the data to get some idea of the sort of analysis that will be appropriate. For this, graphs can be very useful. They may

a) show how the data are distributed,
b) pinpoint outlying values,
c) suggest some form of relationship between variables,
d) indicate an appropriate transformation of the data, or
e) persuade you that further analysis is a waste of time.

3.2 Histograms

3.2.1 A simple histogram

A manufacturer of agricultural fertilizers collected data on the percentages of phosphorus in 138 samples of fertilizer. A simple check on consistency of manufacture is to divide the collection of samples into groups according to the percentage of phosphorus. A series of Genstat statements to do this produces the following output:

```
  1  VARIATE [NVALUES=138] %phos
  2  READ %phos

     Identifier  Minimum  Mean  Maximum  Values  Missing
        %phos      17.76  18.86   19.83     138        0

 17  HISTOGRAM %phos
```

Histogram of %phos

```
           − 17.8      1 *
     17.8 − 18.0      0
     18.0 − 18.2      6 ******
     18.2 − 18.4      8 ********
     18.4 − 18.6     24 ************************
     18.6 − 18.8     26 **************************
     18.8 − 19.0     32 ********************************
     19.0 − 19.2     23 ***********************
     19.2 − 19.4      9 *********
     19.4 − 19.6      6 ******
     19.6 − 19.8      2 **
     19.8 −           1 *
```

Scale: 1 asterisk represents 1 unit.

The READ statement reads the 138 percentages of phosphorus into a variate called %phos (notice that Genstat treats the percent sign (%) as a letter). In the input, these values follow the READ statement, and are terminated by a colon. The READ statement also gives a summary of the data, as in the example of Chapter 1. The values here range from 17.76% to 19.83%. The command HISTOGRAM then divides the values into groups and prints a histogram, using asterisks to represent the values. Genstat sets the number of groups, and the group limits, automatically: the number of groups is approximately the square root of the number of values.

From this histogram it appears that the data are almost Normally distributed (that is, they have a symmetrical, bell-shaped distribution); also that the percentage of phosphorus in most samples varies between 18.4% and 19.2%.

3.2.2 Setting the number of groups

It may be that the number of groups that Genstat sets by default would be too large. Then the HISTOGRAM statement can be modified to give explicitly the number of groups required. For example, suppose that there were 600 values for the percentages of phosphorus, instead of 138, and you wanted to divide these into 15 groups rather than the 25 that would be given by default. You would then put:

```
HISTOGRAM [NGROUPS=15] %phos
```

The constant 15 used for setting the NGROUPS option could be replaced by a scalar identifier as in the following statements:

```
SCALAR Groupno; VALUE=15
HISTOGRAM [NGROUPS=Groupno] %phos
```

3.2.3 Producing parallel histograms

The manufacturer is also interested in the percentage of phosphorus in another series of samples of another batch of fertilizer. A good way to compare the distribution in the two samples is to draw histograms side by side. This is done if both sets of values are given in the same HISTOGRAM statement:

```
HISTOGRAM [NGROUPS=15] %phos,%phos2
```

The output from this modified program is shown below.

```
18  VARIATE [NVALUES=114] %phos2
19  READ %phos2
```

Identifier	Minimum	Mean	Maximum	Values	Missing
%phos2	17.85	18.88	19.85	114	0

```
32  HISTOGRAM [NGROUPS=15] %phos,%phos2
```

Histogram of %phos and %phos2

```
        − 17.85   %phos    1 *
                  %phos2   1 *

  17.85 − 18.00   %phos    0
                  %phos2   1 *

  18.00 − 18.15   %phos    6 ******
                  %phos2   0

  18.15 − 18.30   %phos    0
                  %phos2   4 ****

  18.30 − 18.45   %phos    8 ********
                  %phos2   4 ****

  18.45 − 18.60   %phos   24 ************************
                  %phos2  19 ******************

  18.60 − 18.75   %phos   26 **************************
                  %phos2  23 **********************

  18.75 − 18.90   %phos    0
                  %phos2  15 **************
```

```
18.90 - 19.05    %phos    32 *********************************
                 %phos2    9 *********

19.05 - 19.20    %phos    23 ***********************
                 %phos2   12 ************

19.20 - 19.35    %phos     9 *********
                 %phos2   10 **********

19.35 - 19.50    %phos     6 ******
                 %phos2    8 ********

19.50 - 19.65    %phos     0
                 %phos2    2 **

19.65 - 19.80    %phos     2 **
                 %phos2    5 *****

19.80 -          %phos     1 *
                 %phos2    1 *
```

Scale: 1 asterisk represents 1 unit.

3.2.4 Specifying group limits

A survey of birds gave a distribution of numbers of non-resident species observed in September over several years (*Introductory statistics*, Quenouille, 1950, Butterworth-Springer, London). A useful way to display this distribution is to draw a histogram showing the number of times no species were observed, one species, two species and so on. To produce this with the HISTOGRAM command, it is necessary to specify explicitly the limits of each group. This can be done by supplying a variate, which we shall call Bounds, with the upper bound of each group:

```
VARIATE [NVALUES=160] Nspecies
READ Nspecies
(data) :
VARIATE [VALUES=1,2,3,4,5,6,7,8,9,10,11,12,\
               13,14,15,16,17,18] Bounds
HISTOGRAM [LIMITS=Bounds] Nspecies
```

Note that any Genstat statement may continue over more than one line, using the continuation symbol — backslash ($\setminus$).

You saw in Chapter 1 (Section 1.2.2) how a value can be assigned to a scalar when it is declared. The VARIATE statement above shows how values can be assigned to a variate also; in fact, values can be assigned to any data structure when it is declared.

It is not necessary to declare the length (that is, the number of values) of the variate Bounds explicitly. The values are assigned in the declaration itself, rather than being read in later, and the number of values sets the length of the variate.

Assigning values to a structure when it is declared is especially useful when the values are not in a random order but in some regular arrangement. For example, Genstat permits you to abbreviate arithmetic progressions so that the VARIATE statement above can be written as:

```
VARIATE [VALUES=1 ... 18] Bounds .
```

Such abbreviations are considered in more detail later.

The complete program and the resulting histogram are shown below.

```
1    VARIATE [NVALUES=160] Nspecies
2    READ Nspecies

     Identifier  Minimum  Mean  Maximum  Values  Missing
     Nspecies      1.000  6.631  22.000     160        0

11   VARIATE [VALUES=1...18] Bounds
12   HISTOGRAM [LIMITS=Bounds] Nspecies

Histogram of Nspecies grouped by Bounds

        -   1    6  ******
    1 -   2    6  ******
    2 -   3   15  **************
    3 -   4   26  **************************
    4 -   5   22  **********************
    5 -   6   20  ********************
    6 -   7   13  *************
    7 -   8   14  **************
    8 -   9    9  *********
    9 - 10    7  *******
   10 - 11    2  **
   11 - 12    7  *******
   12 - 13    4  ****
   13 - 14    3  ***
   14 - 15    0
   15 - 16    1  *
   16 - 17    2  **
   17 - 18    1  *
   18 -       2  **

Scale: 1 asterisk represents 1 unit.
```

It is not clear from the labelling what happens at the limits of each group in the histogram. In fact, a value that is exactly equal to a limit is placed in the lower group. Thus, an area with six species is shown in the group labelled 5-6.

The histogram shows that the data have a skew distribution, with most areas having between two and eight species, but some having many more.

3.3 Graphs

3.3.1 Point plots

A sociology student has obtained records of 100 marriages in a registry office, including the ages of the brides and grooms. It is likely that people marry someone of about their own age, and a graph of the recorded ages will show whether this is true. The following statements produce such a graph:

```
VARIATE [NVALUES=100] Bride,Groom
READ Bride,Groom
(data) :
GRAPH Y=Bride; X=Groom
```

A graph shows the relationship between two variates: conventionally, the variate that is plotted up and down the paper is called the *y-variate* and the one plotted across the paper is called the *x-variate*.

The GRAPH statement produces a graph that will fit onto a video screen or onto a sheet of line-printer paper, depending on whether you are using Genstat interactively or in batch (see Chapter 2). To fit the graphs in our examples onto the pages of this book we shall usually set options to specify the size of the frame:

```
GRAPH [NROWS=21; NCOLUMNS=61] Y=Bride; X=Groom
```

In subsequent examples, we shall use these settings without comment, unless we want a graph with different numbers of rows or columns of characters.

On most computer printers, a setting of NROWS=$6r+1$ will give a graph r inches high, and NCOLUMNS=$10c+1$ will give a graph c inches wide.

The graph produced by the statements above is made up of keyboard characters, as shown in the following output, and so can be displayed by any terminal or line printer.

```
1  VARIATE [NVALUES=100] Bride,Groom
2  READ Bride,Groom
```

Identifier	Minimum	Mean	Maximum	Values	Missing
Bride	16.00	25.51	53.00	100	0
Groom	18.00	28.45	65.00	100	0 Skew

16   GRAPH[NROWS=21;NCOLUMNS=61]Y=Bride;X=Groom

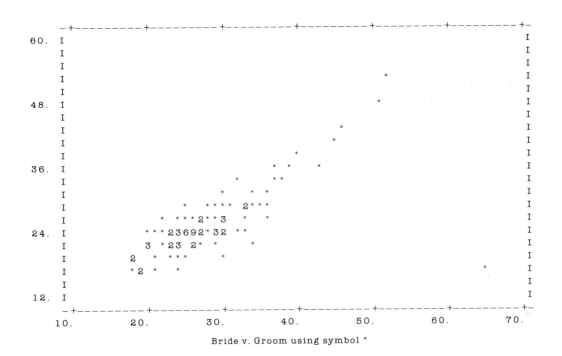

Bride v. Groom using symbol *

The GRAPH statement produces a plot where the scale numbers for the y-axis and the x-axis have been calculated automatically from the values of Bride and Groom. The asterisk (*) is used as plotting symbol, but this is replaced by numbers in the range 1 to 9 at certain locations: these numbers indicate the number of coincident points at those locations. Thus 2 indicates two coincident points, 3 indicates three coincident points, and so on, with the convention that 9 indicates nine coincidences or more. If you count the number of points represented on the plot you will find it is 97 so there must be 9+3 coincidences at the location labelled 9.

It seems, indeed, that people tend to marry others of about the same age; but perhaps the lively old gentleman of 65 and his 18-year-old bride should be excluded from any subsequent statistical analysis!

3.3.2 Smoothed-line plots

The following values were recorded in a study of the growth of sycamore seedlings (*A computer program for fitting the Richards function*, Causton, 1969, Biometrics 25, 401-409).

   a) Weight of seedling
   b) Number of weeks since germination
   c) Predicted weight

The predicted weights were produced by regression analysis, with the sort of method to be described in Chapter 4, using a theoretical relationship of size of tree with time. The values from this study are stored in variates with the statement:

```
READ Weight,Weeks,Predwt
```

The data can be displayed by the following statements:

```
GRAPH Y=Weight; X=Weeks
GRAPH Y=Predwt; X=Weeks
```

However, the predicted values are much better displayed as a line graph, since they are just individual points on a theoretical regression line. This can be done by setting the parameter METHOD:

```
GRAPH Y=Predwt; X=Weeks; METHOD=curve
```

Better still, the observed values can be plotted as points in the same frame by including both variates in one statement:

```
GRAPH Y=Predwt,Weight; X=Weeks; METHOD=curve,point
```

Although two graphs will be drawn, it is only necessary to write Weeks once because the identifier in the second parameter is automatically recycled. This rule applies to all parameters in Genstat commands; it is always the first parameter in the definition of a command that specifies the number of operations — here it is the Y parameter.

If the METHOD parameter is unset, as in the Bride and Groom example above, point plots are provided by default. If it is set to 'curve', Genstat produces the best representation of a line between the points that can be managed on most line printers. The graph produced by the statements is shown below.

```
1  VARIATE [NVALUES=11] Weeks,Weight,Predwt
2  READ Weeks,Weight,Predwt
```

Identifier	Minimum	Mean	Maximum	Values	Missing
Weeks	2.00	12.00	22.00	11	0
Weight	0.390	7.594	23.120	11	0
Predwt	0.449	7.449	24.470	11	0

```
14  GRAPH[NROWS=21;NCOLUMNS=61]Y=Predwt,Weight;X=Weeks;\
        METHOD=curve,point
```

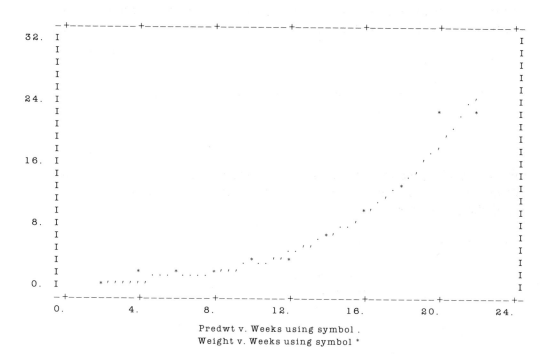

Predwt v. Weeks using symbol .
Weight v. Weeks using symbol *

It can be important to give the variates in the Y parameter in the right order. If a plotted point lies on a curve, GRAPH will print either the symbol for the point or the curve, whichever is specified last. So specify curves first and plots last: it is not important if the plot of an observed value obscures part of a line, but if a line obliterates one of the points there is a serious loss of information.

Notice that the GRAPH statement labels the frame with the identifiers of the variates that are plotted. If this labelling is not sufficient, you can specify titles for the axes by setting options of the GRAPH statement:

```
TEXT [VALUES='Seedling weight —g—'] Yaxis
TEXT [VALUES='Number of weeks from germination'] Xaxis
GRAPH [YTITLE=Yaxis; XTITLE=Xaxis] Y=Predwt,Weight;\
   X=Weeks; METHOD=curve,point
```

To hold the axis titles, a new type of structure called a *text* is used. A text holds a series of textual values called *strings*. A string is just a series of characters, but when it contains any character other than letters and digits (as here, the spaces between words) or starts with a digit, the characters must be enclosed in single quotes. Both text structures here have just one string each; the strings are assigned to the structures Yaxis and Xaxis in the declarations with an option called VALUES, just as for scalars and variates.

The setting of the parameter METHOD also consists of strings — 'curve' and 'point' — but these are not values of a text structure. Strings like these, which come from a list of predefined strings (including 'curve' and 'point' here) never need to be quoted in any statement, though they can be if you want.

You can insert the text for the axis titles directly into the option settings:

```
GRAPH [YTITLE='Seedling weight —g—';\
    XTITLE='Number of weeks from germination'; NROWS=21;\
    NCOLUMNS=61] Y=Predwt,Weight; X=Weeks; METHOD=curve,point
```

This would shorten the program, provided that the texts are not required elsewhere.

The resulting graph is shown below.

```
16  GRAPH [YTITLE='Seedling weight—g—';\
17     XTITLE='Number of weeks from germination'; NROWS=21;\
18     NCOLUMNS=61] Y=Predwt,Weight;X=Weeks;\
19     METHOD=curve,point
```

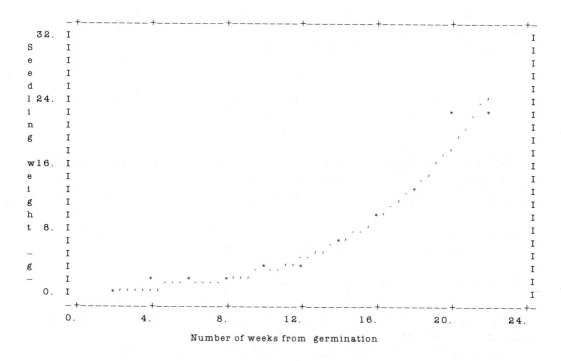

Number of weeks from germination

3.3.3 Unsmoothed lines

To those seeking evidence for popular beliefs it may be of interest to compare human birth-rates with the population of storks in Sweden over the years 1900 to 1935. One way of comparing these is to plot both sets of figures in the same frame. Both sets can be depicted by points representing each year and the points can be joined by lines to indicate the trend. Two lines followed by two point plots are required and these can be specified using the METHOD parameter as in the last example: the setting required to specify an unsmoothed line is 'line'. The statements needed to produce this graph are as follows.

```
VARIATE  [VALUES=1900, 1905, 1910, 1915, 1920, 1925, 1930, 1935] Years
VARIATE  Storks,Births; VALUES=!(81,66,49,42,26,20,12,14),\
    !(27,25.73,24.8,21.62,23.47,17.58,15.23,13.76)
CALCULATE Births = Births * 5 - 60
GRAPH Y=Births,Storks,Births,Storks; X=Years;\
    METHOD=line,line,point,point
```

The values here are included in the declarations of the variates, since there are not many of them. However, the values of Storks and Births are assigned with the VALUES parameter, not the VALUES option. In fact, any declaration with an option called VALUES has a parameter called VALUES as well. (You saw in Chapter 1, Section 1.4, that the SCALAR declaration has an option and a parameter called VALUE — singular, since a scalar has only one value). Either can be used, but the option is usually more convenient for single structures, while the parameter allows different values to be assigned to different structures. When each structure may store many values, it is essential to show where one set of values ends and the next begins; this is done by the combination symbol — the exclamation mark (!) — together with brackets. The values in a VALUES option must not be combined in this way: each structure in a declaration with the VALUES option set is given the full set of values.

The data on births are recorded as numbers of births per thousand people. So that values for birth-rates and pairs of storks can be plotted using the same scale, birth-rates are modified by a CALCULATE statement to give the number of births per 5000 people less 60. Brief titles for the y-axis and the x-axis can be specified by inserting text directly into the YTITLE and XTITLE options of the GRAPH statement. A longer explanatory title can be placed at the top of the frame using another option called TITLE. An appropriate text to head the frame here would be:

```
TEXT T; VALUES='Change in adjusted birthrate and pairs of \
    storks with time'
```

Notice that the VALUES parameter has been used in the declaration. The value does not need to be combined as for the values of the variates above because it is a single value. Notice also that a quoted string can be continued onto the next line with the continuation symbol.

The GRAPH statement then becomes:

```
GRAPH [TITLE=T; YTITLE='Births & storks'; XTITLE='Y E A R']\
    Y=Births,Storks,Births,Storks; X=Years; \
    METHOD=line,line,point,point
```

Genstat will first plot Births against Years, noting that the first setting in the parameter METHOD is 'line' and hence that an unsmoothed line is required. Next Storks will be plotted against Years, Years being recycled since there are no more identifiers in the x-variate list. The second setting in METHOD is also 'line' so again an unsmoothed line is required. The third and fourth strings in METHOD are 'point', so point plots of Birth against Years and Storks against Years will be produced.

If this graph were one of a series for several investigations in different countries it would be useful to have the same scales for all the graphs in the series to make comparison easier. Instead of leaving it to Genstat to work out the scale values, the limits for these values will therefore be specified using options. These will specify that:

> 0 is the lower limit for the y-axis
> 84 is the upper limit for the y-axis
> 1890 is the lower limit for the x-axis
> 1950 is the upper limit for the x-axis

The GRAPH statement becomes:

```
GRAPH [TITLE = T; YTITLE = 'Births & storks'; XTITLE = 'Y E A R'; \
    YLOWER = 0; YUPPER = 84; XLOWER = 1890; XUPPER = 1950; \
    NROWS = 21; NCOLUMNS = 61] Y = Births,Storks,Births,Storks; \
    X = Years; METHOD = line,line,point,point
```

If the GRAPH statement were left at this there would be no way of telling which plot was which. To distinguish them you can specify the symbols you want for each plot, overruling Genstat's default symbols (* for point plots and a mixture of . and ' for lines). You can indicate your chosen symbols for the lines and the plots by setting a further parameter, called SYMBOL. The settings are the symbols required for drawing the graphs, enclosed in single quotes:

```
SYMBOL = '.','.','b','s'
```

This specifies that the two lines will be drawn using the symbol . and the two point plots will be plotted with the symbol b (for births) and s (for storks). The complete program and the results are shown below.

```
 1    VARIATE [VALUES = 1900, 1905, 1910, 1915, 1920, 1925, 1930, \
 2    1935] Years
 3    VARIATE  Storks,Births;VALUES = !(81,66,49,42,26,20,12,14), \
 4       !(27, 25.73, 24.8, 21.62, 23.47, 17.58, 15.23, 13.76)
 5    CALCULATE  Births = Births * 5 − 60
 6    TEXT T; VALUES = 'Change in adjusted birthrate and pairs of \
-7    storks with time'
 8    GRAPH  [TITLE = T;YTITLE = 'Births & storks';XTITLE = 'YEAR'; \
 9       YLOWER = 0;YUPPER = 84;XLOWER = 1890;XUPPER = 1950; \
10       NROWS = 21;NCOLUMNS = 61]  Y = Births,Storks,Births,Storks; \
11       X = Years;METHOD = line,line,point,point;SYMBOL = '.','.','b','s'
```

Change in adjusted birthrate and pairs of storks with time

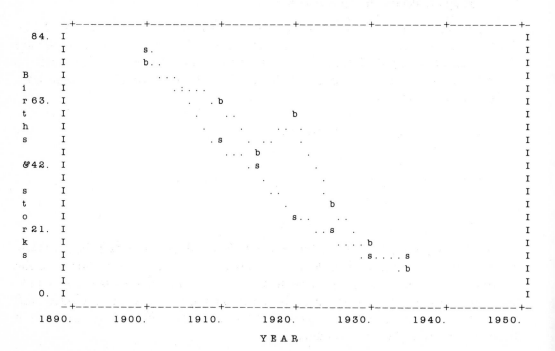

                                    YEAR

3.4 High-quality graphics

So far the histograms and graphs shown were produced on the same printer as the rest of the Genstat output. This is quick and convenient, and such displays are good enough for many purposes, for example to identify outliers or to assess the form of a relationship. But any plotting symbol is located with no more precision than a character in a line of text. This is particularly noticeable when trying to draw a curve — it may look uneven. Devices such as plotters and graphics terminals locate symbols more precisely; also different colours and special plotting symbols can be used. Such high-quality graphics are often essential, for example if the displays are needed for publication. The statements for producing high-quality graphics will now be illustrated by repeating some of the examples from previous sections of this chapter.

3.4.1 High-quality histograms

The directive name for producing histograms on a graphics device is DHISTO-GRAM. The statements to draw a histogram of the fertilizer data in Section 3.2.1 are identical to those already described, apart from this change to the directive name and the inclusion of an OPEN statement (Chapter 2, Section 2.4) to name a file to store the graphical information.

```
VARIATE [NVALUES=138] %phos
READ %phos
   (data) :
OPEN 'PHOSPHOR.GRD'; CHANNEL=1; FILETYPE=graphics
DHISTOGRAM %phos
STOP
```

After running this program, the file PHOSPHOR.GRD will contain the necessary information for your graphical device to draw the picture. You can then send the information to the device using a command in your computer's operating system to use one of the graphical systems available on your computer: ask your computer staff for details. The graph produced by the above statements is shown in Figure 3.1 — it has been reduced to fit on the page.

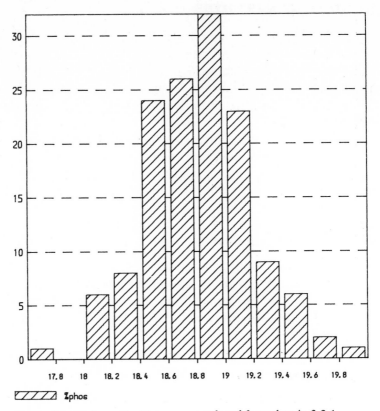

Figure 3.1: High-quality histogram produced from data in 3.2.1

3.4.2 Simple high-quality graphs

For high-quality graphs, the directive name is DGRAPH. No other change is necessary to draw simple point plots in one colour, apart from opening the graphics file. Thus the statements to plot the marriage data are:

```
VARIATE [NVALUES=100] Bride,Groom
READ Bride,Groom
   (data) :
OPEN 'MARRIAGE.GRD'; CHANNEL=1; FILETYPE=graphics
DGRAPH Y=Bride; X=Groom
STOP
```

The resulting graph is shown in Figure 3.2.

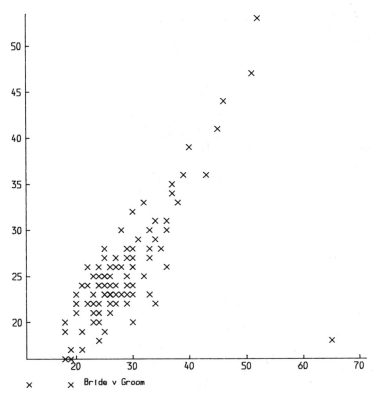

Figure 3.2: High-quality graph produced from data in 3.3.1

3.4.3 Specifying types of graph and colour

For more complex graphs the form of the statement must be changed and additional statements given. The PEN statement specifies how a part of a graph is to be drawn, and links to the PEN parameter of the DGRAPH statement. For example:

```
PEN 1,2; METHOD=monotonic,point
```

sets up two ways of drawing graphs, to be referred to by the pen numbers 1 and 2. Pen 1 will draw monotonic curves between supplied values (there are other ways of drawing curves, not described here) while pen 2 will plot the points only — just as was specified with the METHOD parameter of the GRAPH statement for the line-printer graph. The first pen will use the default colour — black is usually the default on a paper plotter — and the second pen will use the second colour provided on whatever device the graph is drawn. This may be blue, for example, but it is likely to be different on different devices. The colour can be modified by the parameter COLOUR:

```
PEN 1,2; METHOD=monotonic,point; COLOUR=2,4
```

This specifies that the parts of the graph drawn with pen 1 will be in the colour numbered 2, which may be blue, and the parts drawn by pen 2 will be in the colour numbered 4, which may be green. Since this book is printed in black and white, we shall use the following statement:

```
PEN 1,2; METHOD=monotonic,point; COLOUR=1
```

The following program draws the graph of predicted weight of seedlings against time, as in Section 3.3.2.

```
VARIATE [NVALUES=11] Weeks,Weight,Predwt
READ Weeks,Weight,Predwt
  (data) :
OPEN 'SYCAMORE.GRD'; CHANNEL=1; FILETYPE=graphics
PEN 1,2; METHOD=monotonic,point; COLOUR=1
DGRAPH  Y=Predwt,Weight; X=Weeks; PEN=1,2
STOP
```

The resulting graph is shown in Figure 3.3.

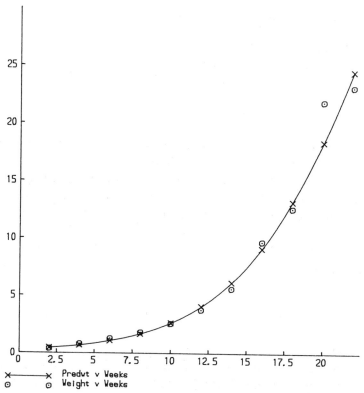

Figure 3.3: High-quality graph with specified type of graph and colour (from data in 3.3.2)

3.4.4 Modifying axes and specifying symbols

The graph of births and numbers of storks against time in Section 3.3.3 included specified titles and axis bounds. A title can be included on a high-quality graph by setting the option TITLE of DGRAPH, just as for the GRAPH statement:

```
DGRAPH [TITLE = T] Y = Births,Storks,Births,Storks; X = Years
```

However, axis titles and bounds for the axes are controlled by a statement called AXES. The AXES statement controls all aspects of the axes of a high-quality graph, including the type of axes and whether any axes are drawn at all. To produce the same axes as the GRAPH statement in Section 3.3.3, the following AXES statement is needed:

```
AXES  WINDOW = 1; YTITLE = 'Births & storks'; XTITLE = 'Y E A R';\
      YLOWER = 0; YUPPER = 84; XLOWER = 1890; XUPPER = 1950
```

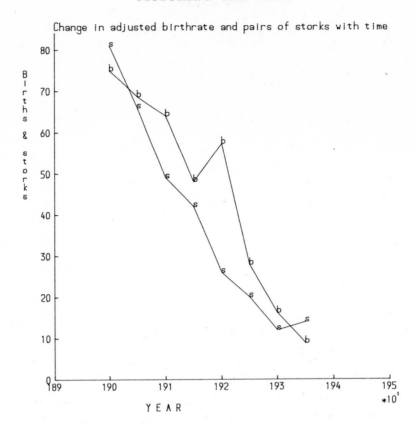

Change in adjusted birthrate and pairs of storks with time

Figure 3.4: High-quality graph with modified axes and specified symbols (from data in 3.3.3)

The AXES statement refers to a window number, which will also be referred to in the DGRAPH statement. In fact, several *windows* or areas within the graphical display can be identified, but we do not describe this here.

A PEN statement is also needed to specify the type of plots; there is a SYMBOL parameter to control the plotting symbol. Two pens are defined: one for drawing a line and putting the symbol 'b' at each point, and the other similarly with the letter 's':

```
PEN 1,2; METHOD=line; SYMBOL='b','s'; COLOUR=1
```

The full program to draw the graph is shown below, and the resulting graph appears in Figure 3.4.

```
VARIATE [VALUES=1900, 1905, 1910, 1915, 1920, 1925, 1930, 1935] Years
VARIATE Storks,Births; VALUES=!(81,66,49,42,26,20,12,14),\
    !(27,25.73,24.8,21.62,23.47,17.58,15.23,13.76)
CALCULATE Births = Births * 5 - 60
TEXT T; VALUES='Change in adjusted birthrate and pairs of \
storks with time'
OPEN 'STORKS.GRD'; CHANNEL=1; FILETYPE=graphics
AXES WINDOW=1; YTITLE='Births & storks'; XTITLE='Y E A R'; \
    YLOWER=0; YUPPER=84; XLOWER=1890; XUPPER=1950
PEN 1,2; METHOD=line; SYMBOL='b','s'; COLOUR=1
DGRAPH [TITLE=T; WINDOW=1] Y=Births,Storks; X=Years; PEN=1,2
STOP
```

3.5 Summary

Chapter 3 describes statements to produce histograms, point plots and lines.
Histograms are produced by statements of the form:

HISTOGRAM [options] list of variates
DHISTOGRAM [options] list of variates

By default, the number of groups for each histogram is approximately equal to the square root of the number of values for the variate from which the histogram is formed. The option NGROUPS specifies the number of groups explicitly, and the option LIMITS specifies a variate of group limits.

Text structures, to store strings of characters, are defined by statements of the form:

TEXT [VALUES=strings] identifiers; VALUES=quoted strings or texts

Point plots and lines, suitable for line printers, are produced by statements of the form:

GRAPH [options] Y=variates; X=variates; METHOD=strings; SYMBOL=texts

If the parameter METHOD is omitted, point plots of the y-variates against the x-variates are obtained. If lines, or a mixture of point plots and lines, are required then the METHOD parameter must be specified. This can contain the following strings: 'point' (for point plots), 'line' (for unsmoothed lines) and 'curve' (for smoothed lines).

If the SYMBOL parameter is omitted, a mixture of the symbols . and ' is used for drawing lines and the symbol * for plotting points. Other plotting symbols can be specified as texts or quoted strings.

The GRAPH statement includes the following options:

TITLE	Specifies a title for the graph
YTITLE, XTITLE	Specify titles for the y-axis and x-axis
YLOWER, XLOWER	Specify lower boundary values for the axis scales
YUPPER, XUPPER	Specify upper boundary values
NROWS, NCOLUMNS	Specify the number of rows and number of columns per frame

Plots suitable for high-quality graphics devices are produced by statements of the following form:

DGRAPH [options] Y=variates; X=variates; PEN=scalars

The TITLE option of DGRAPH specifies a title for the plot, and the WINDOW option refers to a set of axes defined by the AXES statement.

High-quality graphs are modified by statements of the form:

PEN scalars; COLOUR=scalars; METHOD=strings; SYMBOL=texts
AXES WINDOW=scalar; YTITLE=text; XTITLE=scalar;
    YLOWER=scalar; YUPPER=scalar; XLOWER=scalar;
     XUPPER=scalar

The settings of the METHOD parameter of the PEN statement include 'point', 'line' and 'monotonic'.

3.6 Exercises

3(1) A tall variety and a dwarf variety of pea were hybridized and seeds were obtained from the hybrid plants. Forty of these seeds were sown and the heights of the plants obtained were measured. The heights (in metres) were prepared for reading by Genstat as shown below.

```
0.55  1.26  0.53  0.26  1.23  1.15  0.31  1.22  1.13  0.39
1.10  1.06  1.10  0.43  1.18  0.81  0.99  1.25  0.18  1.13
1.09  1.24  1.35  1.14  1.29  1.10  1.25  1.14  1.14  0.30
1.22  0.25  0.15  1.15  1.17  1.45  1.20  1.33  1.16  1.11 :
```

Write a program to produce a histogram showing the distribution of plant height.

3(2) A psychologist wished to test the theory that motivation influences performance at games of skill. Fifteen subjects obtained scores out of 100 for shooting at a target. The motivation of each subject was measured, firstly on a scale from 0 to 9 after an interview with the psychologist and secondly by means of his galvanic skin response (GSR). These data were prepared for analysis with Genstat as follows.

```
25  8  0.82  32  7  1.08  62  6  0.71  40  1  0.28  25  1  0.33
52  7  0.89  56  6  0.84  55  3  0.41  60  2  0.49  47  2  0.42
12  1  0.17  89  4  0.44  15  7  1.06  83  6  0.71  88  5  0.46 :
```

For each subject the shooting score is given first, followed by the motivation score, followed by the GSR (measured in microamps). Write a Genstat program that produces scatter diagrams of shooting score against motivation score and of shooting score against GSR. Give suitable titles to the axes, and use the same bounds for the shooting score axis in both graphs.

3(3) A power station kept monthly records of its production of electricity and of the outdoor temperature for a year. These records were prepared for reading by Genstat as follows.

```
 1  561  -1   2  522   3  3  466   6  4  413   8   5  317  13
 6  236  16   7  245  16  8  312  13  9  305  14  10  367  10
11  521   2  12  562   0 :
```

The first column represents the month of the year, the second the rate of production of electricity (in megawatts) and the third the temperature (in °C). Write a Genstat program to draw unsmoothed lines showing how electricity production and temperature are related to time. The axes should have suitable titles and should all start at zero except for the temperature axis.

Produce another graph with the two lines in the same frame; also include the observations using the symbol E for electricity production and T for temperature. You will need to change the units in which electricity production is expressed or the fluctuations in temperature will be almost imperceptible.

4 Linear regression analysis

4.1 Introduction

If a preliminary graphical inspection of your data shows that further analysis is worth while, one of the statistical techniques that you may wish to use is regression analysis. This is a method used in many fields of study to examine the way in which one variable changes in response to others. For example, in Section 4.2 we shall look at the way in which people's blood-pressure changes as they get older. The technique can help to identify relationships between variables, to predict one variable from others or to provide a descriptive summary of a set of data. This is not the place for a full introduction to regression analysis, but if you are unfamiliar with the method you could read *Statistical methods* (Snedecor & Cochran, 1980, Iowa State University Press, Ames), or for a fuller account *Applied regression analysis* (Draper & Smith, 1981, Wiley, New York).

There are extensive facilities in Genstat for analysing regression models. In this chapter, we consider the commonest forms of linear regression analysis in detail, and show how regression analyses can be specified in Genstat with a few compact statements.

4.2 Fitting a regression model

4.2.1 Choosing the model

We have recordings of blood-pressure from a sample of 38 women whose ages range from 20 to 80. The data can best be displayed in a graph of pressure against age, such as is produced by the following Genstat statements:

```
VARIATE [NVALUES=38] Pressure,Age
READ [PRINT=data,summary] Pressure,Age
  82.17 28    88.19 46    89.66 63    81.45 36    85.16 42
  89.77 59    89.11 54   107.96 77    74.82 21    83.98 57
  92.95 47    79.51 34    87.86 51    76.85 27    76.93 24
  87.09 41    97.55 66    92.04 69   100.85 72    96.3  60
  86.42 50    94.16 57    78.12 32    89.06 59    94.58 74
 103.48 77    81.3  41    83.71 36    68.38 20    86.64 47
  87.91 51    86.42 57   103.87 69    83.76 36    84.35 54
  68.64 24   100.5  61   100.42 80 :
GRAPH [YTITLE='Blood pressure'; XTITLE='Age'] Y=Pressure; X=Age
```

The GRAPH statement will be familiar from Chapter 3, but the READ statement includes an option that you have not met before. Many statements in Genstat have an option called PRINT and these options are all concerned with specifying what information to display on the output. A PRINT option can have several settings in a single statement, each referring to a particular section of printing. In a READ statement, the settings 'data' and 'summary' correspond respectively to a copy of the data, and to a summary of the minimum, mean, and maximum values. You have seen examples of the summary already in Chapters 1 and 3, since this is the default output. When more than one setting of an option is used in a single statement, all the settings are in force simultaneously: they are not used successively in parallel with the lists of parameters. Thus, the data and the summary will be printed here for both the variates Pressure and Age; not the data only for Pressure and the summary only for Age. Here is the output from the above statements:

```
 1   VARIATE [NVALUES=38] Pressure,Age
 2   READ [PRINT=data,summary] Pressure,Age
 3    82.17  28    88.19  46    89.66  63    81.45  36    85.16  42
 4    89.77  59    89.11  54   107.96  77    74.82  21    83.98  57
 5    92.95  47    79.51  34    87.86  51    76.85  27    76.93  24
 6    87.09  41    97.55  66    92.04  69   100.85  72    96.3   60
 7    86.42  50    94.16  57    78.12  32    89.06  59    94.58  74
 8   103.48  77    81.3   41    83.71  36    68.38  20    86.64  47
 9    87.91  51    86.42  57   103.87  69    83.76  36    84.35  54
10    68.64  24   100.5   61   100.42  80 :
```

Identifier	Minimum	Mean	Maximum	Values	Missing
Pressure	68.38	87.95	107.96	38	0
Age	20.00	49.97	80.00	38	0

```
11   GRAPH[YTITLE='Blood pressure';XTITLE='Age';\
12       NROWS=21;NCOLUMNS=61]Y=Pressure;X=Age
```

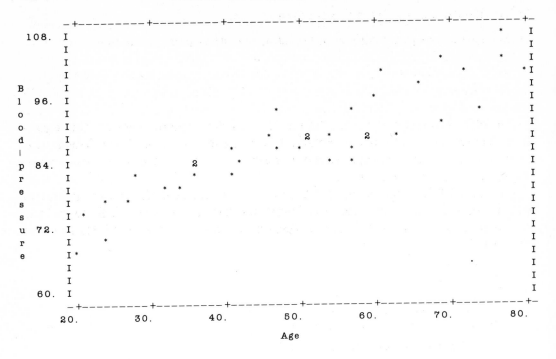

The graph shows clearly that there is a fairly linear relationship between blood-pressure and age. This can be quantified in terms of a linear regression model, which specifies a *line of best fit* or *regression line* through these points. For the *i*th woman in the sample, the equation of the line is

$$\text{pressure}_i = a + b \times \text{age}_i + e_i$$

where *a* can be visualized as the intercept of the regression line, *b* as its slope and e_i is the vertical distance of the *i*th point from the line.

A regression analysis produces estimates of the *parameters a* and *b* of this model, and also of the variance of the variable *e* which is often of as much interest as the parameters. The details of the method of estimation, and of the assumptions that are necessary to fit the model, are dealt with in many standard texts (such as *Applied Regression Analysis*).

4.2.2 Estimating the parameters

To get an analysis of this model in Genstat, two statements are needed:

```
MODEL Pressure
FIT Age
```

The MODEL statement gives the identifier of the *response variate* in the regression, whose variation is to be explained or modelled in terms of age. This is also known as the y-variate because conventionally it is plotted on the vertical or y-axis of a graph, or as the dependent variate.

When the FIT statement supplies the identifier of the *explanatory variate* (known also as the x-variate, covariate or independent variate) the model is fitted and the results of an analysis printed. The regression analysis produced by this statement is shown below:

```
13  MODEL Pressure
14  FIT Age

14  ....................................................................................................

***** Regression Analysis *****

Response variate: Pressure
     Fitted terms: Constant, Age

*** Summary of analysis ***

               d.f.      s.s.      m.s.
Regression        1    2647.7   2647.69
  Residual       36     561.6     15.60
     Total       37    3209.3     86.74

Percentage variance accounted for 82.0

* MESSAGE: The following units have high leverage:
                        29              0.111
                        38              0.111

*** Estimates of regression coefficients ***

             estimate     s.e.       t
Constant        63.04     2.02    31.27
     Age       0.4983   0.0382    13.03
```

The regression analysis is preceded by a line of dots labelled with the line number given to the FIT statement. This is a useful landmark when several statements giving output follow one another.

The first section of the output gives the analysis of variance of the observations of pressure, which will now be examined in more detail. The column headed 'm.s.' (mean square) shows how much variation is attributable to the linear dependence on age and how much is left over or 'Residual'. The last line gives a useful summary statistic, the *percentage variance accounted for*. It is the difference between residual and total mean squares, expressed as a percentage of the total mean square. When expressed as a proportion rather than as a percentage, this statistic is called the *adjusted* R^2; it is not quite the same as R^2, the squared coefficient of multiple correlation. The adjustment is for the number of coefficients in the model compared to the number of observations: R^2 increases whenever another variate is added to the model whereas adjusted R^2 increases only if the variate improves the fit more than would be expected by chance.

A warning is printed after this analysis to draw attention to two values with high *leverage*. The leverage is a measure of influence of individual observations on the line of best fit. If some points are much more influential than others, the line is effectively determined just by the influential ones — a very important condition in interpreting the results of the analysis. Genstat warns you about observations with more than twice the average leverage: the average is

    number of parameters / number of observations

which is 2/38, or 0.0526 here. Therefore, the two observations are only just above the criterion.

After the analysis of variance come the estimates of the parameters in the model. So the estimate of a, the intercept or *constant term*, is 63.04 and the standard error of the estimate is 2.02. Similarly b, the slope or *regression coefficient* of Age, is 0.4983 with standard error 0.0382. Genstat also prints a t-statistic for each coefficient, which can be used to test whether it is significantly different from zero. The t-statistic for the slope is large (13.03), indicating that there is a significant association between pressure and age, as we expect from the graph. In order to check this formally you need to know the number of degrees of freedom, which is given in the analysis of variance table in the output, as the entry for 'Residual' in the 'd.f.' column. The number in this case is 36, so you could look up the corresponding values of t in a table such as Table *III* of *Statistical tables* (Fisher & Yates, 1963, Longman, London) or Table 3 of *New Cambridge elementary statistical tables* (Lindley & Scott, 1984, Cambridge University Press). You would find that the probability of a greater value of t is less than 0.1%.

4.2.3 Depicting the line of best fit

In order to see how regression analysis has estimated a line of best fit through the data points it would be useful to plot this line in the scatter diagram of blood-pressure against age. The simplest way to do this in Genstat is to find out the estimated blood-pressure for every woman in the sample, based on the equation:

$$(\text{estimated pressure})_i = a + b \times \text{age}_i$$

These estimated pressures are called the *fitted values* of the regression model: each one differs from the corresponding observed pressure by the term e_i, which is called the *residual*. If you plot the fitted values of blood-pressure against age and join up the points with a straight line, this gives the line of best fit on the graph.

The fitted values of the response variate can be saved after a regression analysis by adding the statement:

```
RKEEP FITTEDVALUES=F
```

The RKEEP statement accesses the results of the latest regression analysis and stores them in data structures. The parameter name FITTEDVALUES indicates that the fitted values are to be kept, and the parameter setting F is to be the identifier of a variate storing them. There is no need to declare F with a VARIATE statement: Genstat automatically makes it a variate of the correct length.

The subsequent statements that produce an appropriate graph, and their output, are as follows:

```
15  RKEEP FITTEDVALUES=F
16  GRAPH[YTITLE='Blood|pressure';XTITLE='Age';NROWS=21;
17      NCOLUMNS=61]Y=F,Pressure;X=Age;METHOD=line,point
```

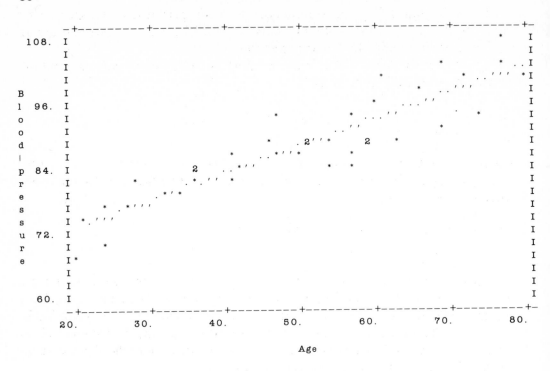

Age

4.3 Regression through the origin

4.3.1 Showing that the intercept is close to zero

The example in Section 4.2 showed how to fit the commonest regression model with the minimum of printing to summarize the results. But you may often need to take account of special features in your data and you may want more information about the regression than an analysis of variance can provide. There is a wide range of options that can be set in the basic regression statements you have just seen, to alter the default form of the analysis. In this section and the next, some of these options are illustrated.

A flame photometer is an instrument that can be used to measure the concentration of sodium in chemical samples. It needs calibration before analysing unknown concentrations and so standard samples are tested first, to provide a 'calibration curve' for converting further measurements into actual concentrations. The results of such a calibration trial are given below:

concentration	25	50	75	100	125	151	175	200	225
instrument reading	10	20	29.5	39.5	52	62	72	83.5	91.5

We know that the scale of measurement of the reading is linear with respect to the sodium concentration — the calibration curve is a straight line — so we can estimate the parameters of the line by linear regression.

Using Genstat to analyse these data, we start by setting up variates to hold the observations and reading the values:

```
VARIATE [NVALUES=9] Sodium,Reading
READ Sodium,Reading
```

The READ statement as it stands will work if the data matrix is presented unit by unit, as you have seen in examples before, so the data values would have to be reordered, thus:

```
 25 10   50 20   75 29.5   100 39.5   125 52   151 62
175 72   200 83.5   225 91.5 :
```

(Notice that any number of values may be put on one line so long as there is at least one space between any two values.) It is easy to avoid this reordering of the data, which can be tedious when there are many values. All you need is to set an option in READ to say that the data are presented in series rather than in parallel — all values for one structure are followed by all values for the other, rather than the first value for each followed by the second for each, and so on.

```
READ [SERIAL=yes] Sodium,Reading
25 50 75 100 125 151 175 200 225:
10 20 29.5 39.5 52 62 72 83.5 91.5:
```

Notice that there must be a colon (:) at the end of the data for each structure when reading serially, since Genstat must be able to confirm where one structure ends and the next begins.

We can now fit the regression model with two statements as in the previous section:

```
MODEL Reading
FIT Sodium
```

These statements produce the following analysis:

```
***** Regression Analysis *****

Response variate:  Reading
Fitted terms:      Constant, Sodium
```

*** Summary of analysis ***

	d.f.	s.s.	m.s.
Regression	1	6489.855	6489.8555
Residual	7	6.033	0.8619
Total	8	6495.889	811.9861

Percentage variance accounted for 99.9

*** Estimates of regression coefficients ***

	estimate	s.e.	t
Constant	−0.901	0.675	−1.34
Sodium	0.41573	0.00479	86.78

The linear model obviously fits very closely. It is also clear that the constant term (intercept) in the model is small: looking up the t-statistic in a table shows that it is not significantly different from zero. This often happens when one variable is regressed on another that measures the same thing in different units, and it is then sensible to fit a model without the unnecessary parameter:

$$\text{reading}_i = b \times \text{sodium}_i + e_i$$

4.3.2 Eliminating the intercept from the model

To fit a model with its constant or intercept set to zero, the CONSTANT option is set in the FIT statement. The default setting is CONSTANT=estimate, and as the option was not set explicitly in the previous examples, the constant term was then estimated. To set the intercept to zero, put:

```
FIT [CONSTANT=omit] Sodium
```

This statement produces the following output:

***** Regression Analysis *****

Response variate: Reading
Fitted terms: Sodium

*** Summary of analysis ***

	d.f.	s.s.	m.s.
Regression	1	29999.430	3.000E+04
Residual	8	7.570	0.946E+00
Total	9	30007.000	3.334E+03

Percentage variance accounted for 99.9

* MESSAGE: The following units have high leverage:

8	0.22
9	0.28

*** Estimates of regression coefficients ***

	estimate	s.e.	t
Sodium	0.41004	0.00230	178.05

The number '3.000E+04' means 3.000×10^4 in exponent notation. This notation is useful when numbers having different orders of magnitude are tabulated.

The analysis of variance table is now uncorrected for the mean. (In other words, the total s.s. is the sum of the squares of the response-variate values, rather than the usual sum of squares of deviations of these values from their mean.) You can see that the total degrees of freedom equals the number of observations, rather than this number minus one as in the last analysis. This form must be used for an analysis with no intercept but it is usually preferable to have a corrected table when the intercept is estimated.

Notice that the two observations with the largest values of the explanatory variable are particularly influential; this is a consequence of forcing the line to pass through the origin. In fact, it is likely that the variance of the residuals is not constant here — the readings vary from 10 up to 91.5, and it seems unlikely that there is the same amount of uncertainty about 10 as there is about 91.5. Therefore, the residuals should be investigated by the methods illustrated in Section 4.5. (See also Exercise 4(1) and its solution in the Appendix.)

4.4 Multiple regression

4.4.1 Fitting polynomial curves by linear regression

In the last two examples it was easy to tell which regression model should be fitted, but when several variables are involved it becomes more difficult. For this reason the regression statements in Genstat are designed for convenient fitting of a sequence of models. We shall illustrate this by investigating some data on house prices and by setting up a model that could be used for prediction of the prices of other houses.

Data about 20 similar houses for sale in Harpenden in 1977 were collected from descriptive sheets provided by estate agents. We shall consider the following variables that are likely to be related to the price:

  a) total floor-space of the house (square metres),
  b) age of the house (years), and
  c) area of the garden (square metres).

Since the increase or decrease in house prices caused by these variables may follow a curve and not a straight line, we shall also consider the square of each variable so that quadratic curves can be tried:

  d) floor-space squared,
  e) age squared, and
  f) garden area squared.

Quadratic models can also be fitted by the methods of linear regression. This apparent paradox is just due to the terminology: linear regression models are linear in the *parameters*, but do not have to be linear in the variables. The model

$$y = a + b \times x + c \times x^2$$

is linear in terms of a, b and c (the parameters), though it is not linear in x. In fact more complex polynomials than the quadratic can be fitted by this method if needed.

The first statements in a Genstat program to carry out the regression analysis will calculate the squares of the variables:

```
VARIATE [NVALUES=20] House,Price,Space,Garden,Age
READ [PRINT=data,summary] House,Price,Space,Garden,Age
(data) :
VARIATE [NVALUES=20] Space2,Garden2,Age2
CALCULATE Space2 = Space ** 2
CALCULATE Garden2 = Garden ** 2
CALCULATE Age2 = Age ** 2
```

Before doing any analysis we shall divide the prices (in pounds) by a factor of 1000 so that the sums of squares in the analysis do not become too large to read easily:

```
CALCULATE Price = Price / 1000
```

It is possible to remind ourselves on the output that this has been done, by declaring Price explicitly:

```
VARIATE [MODIFY=yes] Price; EXTRA=' in thousands of pounds'
```

The 'yes' setting of the option MODIFY ensures that although the VARIATE statement follows the READ statement it does not in fact wipe out the values that have just been read. The EXTRA parameter causes the text to be printed on the output at the start of each regression analysis when the identifier Price is displayed, as can be seen below.

4.4.2 The correlation matrix

To get an initial idea of the importance of each variable we shall look at the correlation coefficient of each of them with price. These can be obtained by the statements:

```
MODEL Price
TERMS [PRINT=correlations] Space,Space2,Garden,Garden2,Age,Age2
```

The TERMS statement not only calculates the correlation coefficients between all the variables in it and those in the MODEL statement; it also performs other preliminary calculations, and must be given when a sequence of regression models is to be fitted.

The first section of a program to analyse these data, and the output that it produces, are then as follows:

```
1  VARIATE[NVALUES=20]House,Price,Space,Garden,Age
2  READ [PRINT=data,summary] House,Price,Space,Garden,Age

3   1  11500  131  140  88
4   2  15500  154  245  70
5   3  12950  137  150  66
6   4  14000  121  180  43
7   5  16500  135  260  17
8   6  17600  172  400  23
9   7  12450  112   90  52
10  8  15500  124  120  10
11  9  14900  141  180  43
12 10  16250  149  350  36
13 11  18400  170  320   7
14 12  11950   93  350  19
15 13  10400  111  280  62
16 14  17250  162  380  12
17 15  13450  148  190  23
18 16  10950  128  160  75
19 17  13950  152   95  92
```

```
20  18        *   113  110  61
21  19  11500  101  450  42
22  20  17500  145  275   0:
```

Identifier	Minimum	Mean	Maximum	Values	Missing
House	1.00	10.50	20.00	20	0
Price	10400	14342	18400	20	1
Space	93.0	135.0	172.0	20	0
Garden	90.0	236.3	450.0	20	0
Age	0.00	42.05	92.00	20	0

```
23  VARIATE [NVALUES=20] Space2,Garden2,Age2
24  CALCULATE  Space2 = Space**2
25  CALCULATE  Garden2 = Garden**2
26  CALCULATE  Age2 = Age**2
27  CALCULATE  Price = Price/1000
28  VARIATE [MODIFY=yes] Price; EXTRA=' in thousands of pounds'
29  MODEL  Price
30  TERMS [PRINT=correlations] Space,Space2,Garden,Garden2,Age,Age2
```

*** Degrees of freedom ***

Correlations: 17

*** Correlation matrix ***

Price	1	1.000					
Space	2	0.768	1.000				
Space2	3	0.778	0.996	1.000			
Garden	4	0.309	0.106	0.167	1.000		
Garden2	5	0.258	0.062	0.127	0.983	1.000	
Age	6	—0.642	—0.164	—0.195	—0.498	—0.449	1.000
Age2	7	—0.547	—0.067	—0.099	—0.534	—0.489	0.965	1.000
		1	2	3	4	5	6	7

Notice that the price of house number 18 is not given, as none was quoted on the estate agent's information sheet. The price is recorded as an asterisk (*) which is the standard way of representing a *missing value* in Genstat. You can see in the summary for the variate Price given by the READ statement that this missing value has been noticed.

The option PRINT=correlations in the TERMS statement has caused the *correlation matrix* to be printed. The degrees of freedom are given for testing the significance of the correlation coefficient between any pair of variables. The number of degrees of freedom is defined to be the number of pairs of values used to calculate the coefficient minus 2. There are 19 pairs here, since the house with no quoted price is automatically excluded from the regression and correlation calculations.

The matrix gives the correlation coefficients between all pairs of variables in the TERMS statement, including the correlations with Price which are of interest here. The rows and columns are numbered 1 to 7 and correspond to the variables. For example, the correlation between price and floor-space is 0.768.

4.4.3 Dropping a variable

Since floor-space and floor-space squared have the highest correlations with price, fitting a quadratic regression model of price on space will be tried first:

```
FIT [PRINT=model,summary] Space,Space2
```

The TERMS statement that was used to get the correlation matrix contains all the variables that will be needed for this and subsequent models. This is essential because of the preliminary calculations that this statement performs. The PRINT option here requests that only a description of the model and a summary of the fit (including a summary analysis of variance) should be printed, since that will give sufficient information for comparing models at this stage. The default setting of this option also includes the word 'estimates' corresponding to the table of regression coefficients with standard errors.

```
31  FIT [PRINT=model,summary] Space,Space2

31  ................................................................................................

***** Regression Analysis *****

Response variate:  Price in thousands of pounds
Fitted terms:      Constant, Space, Space2

*** Summary of analysis ***

              d.f.      s.s.      m.s.
Regression     2       68.55    34.273
Residual      16       43.76     2.735
Total         18      112.31     6.239

Change        -2      -68.55    34.273

Percentage variance accounted for 56.2
```

* MESSAGE: The following units have high leverage:

6	0.39
11	0.32
12	0.54

Since the model

$$\text{price}_i = a + b \times \text{space}_i + c \times \text{space}_i^2 + e_i$$

has a constant term (a) and two regression coefficients (b and c) the regression sum of squares has two degrees of freedom.

There is an extra line now in the summary analysis of variance. It is included when a TERMS statement has been given, and it shows the change in the residual s.s. since the last model fitted. Here, it just compares the model with a null model containing only a constant, but later it will be more useful.

We can now check whether it is necessary to include the quadratic term in the equation, by modifying the model and getting a second analysis. There are several statements available in Genstat to modify regressions in different ways. The DROP statement will be used to reduce the number of terms:

```
32   DROP [PRINT=model,summary] Space2

32   ...................................................................................................
```

***** Regression Analysis *****

Response variate: Price in thousands of pounds
Fitted terms: Constant, Space

*** Summary of analysis ***

	d.f.	s.s.	m.s.
Regression	1	66.22	66.223
Residual	17	46.08	2.711
Total	18	112.31	6.239
Change	1	2.32	2.322

Percentage variance accounted for 56.6

* MESSAGE: The following units have high leverage:

12	0.26

The 'Change' line in this output shows the changes in the residual d.f., s.s. and m.s. since fitting the previous regression model. Because the difference between the two models is the presence or absence of the quadratic term Space2, the changes are due to this term. In fact, this table shows that the quadratic term is unimportant. Formally, you can carry out an *F*-test by dividing the mean square in the line headed 'Change' by the residual mean square of the fuller of the two models, which is the first one here. Comparing the resulting *F*-value, 0.84, with tabulated values (such as in Table *V* of *Statistical Tables*) shows that there is no evidence of a quadratic effect. A more powerful test could be done later when the effects of the other variables affecting the price have been allowed for.

4.4.4 Adding variables

Next we shall include terms in the model to allow for the effect of the different ages of the houses:

$$\text{price}_i = a + b \times \text{space}_i + c \times \text{age}_i + d \times \text{age}_i^2 + e_i$$

A statement called ADD modifies models by increasing the number of terms; we use it twice to get an analysis after each variable is included:

```
33  ADD [PRINT=model,summary] Age

33  .................................................................................................

***** Regression Analysis *****

Response variate:  Price in thousands of pounds
Fitted terms:      Constant, Space, Age

*** Summary of analysis ***

                d.f.       s.s.       m.s.
Regression        2       96.88     48.4394
Residual         16       15.43      0.9642
Total            18      112.31      6.2392

Change           -1      -30.66     30.6555

Percentage variance accounted for 84.5

* MESSAGE: The following units have large residuals:
                      15                    -2.82

* MESSAGE: The following units have high leverage:
                      12                     0.33

34  ADD [PRINT=model,summary] Age2

34  .................................................................................................
```

```
***** Regression Analysis *****

Response variate:   Price in thousands of pounds
Fitted terms:       Cotant, Space, Age, Age2

*** Summary of analysis ***

                d.f.      s.s.      m.s.
Regression        3     97.04    32.347
Residual         15     15.27     1.018
Total            18    112.31     6.239

Change           —1     —0.16     0.162

Percentage variance accounted for 83.7

  * MESSAGE: The following units have large residuals:
                          15              —2.72

  * MESSAGE: The following units have high leverage:
                          17               0.46
```

The summary of both these models includes a warning about one of the observations: number 15 has a high residual, and so does not lie as close to the fitted model as the other observations. The residual values here are standardized so that they are expected to have a standard Normal distribution if the response variable has a Normal distribution. Genstat prints a warning when any of these residuals is unduly large — here, greater than about 2.0 in magnitude.

Clearly the age is very important, but again there is no indication of a quadratic effect on the price.

4.4.5 Switching variables

We can drop the last quadratic term and proceed to try the effect of the remaining variable, the size of the garden. This can be done with a single statement called SWITCH which combines the action of ADD and DROP:

```
35  SWITCH [PRINT=model,summary] Age2,Garden,Garden2

35  ..............................................................................................

***** Regression Analysis *****

Response variate:   Price in thousands of pounds
Fitted terms:       Constant, Space, Age, Garden, Garden2
```

*** Summary of analysis ***

	d.f.	s.s.	m.s.
Regression	4	97.06	24.264
Residual	14	15.25	1.089
Total	18	112.31	6.239
Change	—1	—0.02	0.016

Percentage variance accounted for 82.5

* MESSAGE: The following units have large residuals:

15	—2.79

* MESSAGE: The following units have high leverage:

19	0.67

The SWITCH statement automatically drops the variates named in it that were already in the model — Age2 in this case — and adds those that were not — Garden and Garden2. Comparing this analysis with the one produced by the first ADD statement shows that there is very little association between the size of the garden and the price, once the effect of floor-space and age have been taken into account.

Thus a final regression statement is given, to drop the effects of garden area:

```
36  DROP [PRINT=estimates] Garden,Garden2

36  ........................................................................................
```

***** Regression Analysis *****

*** Estimates of regression coefficients ***

	estimate	s.e.	t
Constant	5.83	1.55	3.76
Space	0.0767	0.0106	7.25
Age	—0.04682	0.00830	—5.64

It is sensible to look at more details of the final fitted model than just the summary and the estimates. For example, The PRINT option of the DROP statement above could be set to include 'fittedvalues' to produce a table giving the observed, fitted, and residual values. However, the information can be displayed without fitting the model again: the statement RDISPLAY shows results of the latest fit, and has a PRINT option with the same possible settings as FIT and the other fitting statements. Here is the table of fitted values produced by RDISPLAY:

37   RDISPLAY[PRINT = fittedvalues]

37   ....

***** Regression Analysis *****

*** Fitted values and residuals ***

| | | | Standardized | | |
Unit	Response	Fitted	value	residual	Leverage
1	11.50		11.75	—0.29	0.21
2	15.50		14.36	1.27	0.17
3	12.95		13.24	—0.31	0.10
4	14.00		13.09	0.96	0.08
5	16.50		15.38	1.20	0.09
6	17.60		17.94	—0.39	0.21
7	12.45		11.98	0.51	0.12
8	15.50		14.87	0.70	0.15
9	14.90		14.63	0.29	0.06
10	16.25		15.57	0.72	0.07
11	18.40		18.53	—0.16	0.23
12	11.95		12.07	—0.15	0.33
13	10.40		11.44	—1.14	0.14
14	17.25		17.69	—0.49	0.17
15	13.45		16.10	—2.82	0.09
16	10.95		12.13	—1.29	0.13
17	13.95		13.18	0.94	0.29
18	*		11.64	*	0.00
19	11.50		11.61	—0.12	0.19
20	17.50		16.95	0.62	0.17
Mean	14.34		14.34	0.00	0.16

Each residual is given by the formula:

$$\text{residual}_i = \frac{\text{observed}_i - \text{fitted}_i}{s \sqrt{(1 - \text{leverage}_i)}}$$

where s is the square root of the current estimate of the variance of the residuals.

Notice that a fitted value has been calculated for house number 18 even though the price was not known: it is the expected price for a house with the recorded floor space and age, based on the information from the other houses.

The size of the t-statistics for the regression coefficients of space and age shows that each term has a significant effect when the effect of the other is eliminated. Hence both terms are necessary in the model to explain the variation in house price. The final percentage variance accounted for is 84% which seems reasonable, given that style, fashion and whim (not to mention double-glazing!) are likely to influence price to some extent.

4.5 Testing the assumptions of regression analysis

It was mentioned at the beginning of this chapter that regression analysis is based on several important assumptions. One of these is that the residuals, e_i, are independently and identically distributed as Normal random variables. In particular the distributions should have the same variance, so for example the expected variability of the price should not be greater for expensive houses than for cheap ones. One way to check this assumption empirically is to plot the residuals against the values fitted by the model to see if there is any obvious relationship between the two:

```
38  RKEEP FITTEDVALUES=F;RESIDUALS=R
39  GRAPH [YTITLE='Residual';XTITLE='Fittedprice';\
40        NROWS=21;NCOLUMNS=61] Y=R;X=F
```

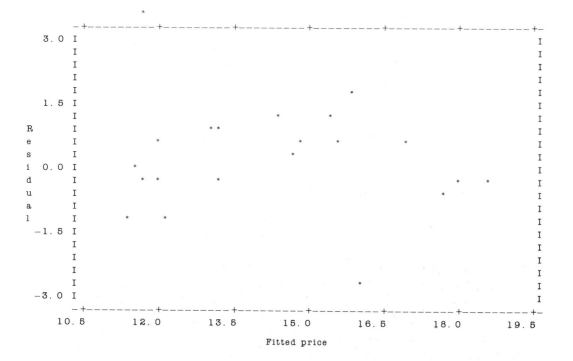

Fitted price

Notice that one point is plotted outside the frame: it corresponds to house number 18 whose price is not known.

It is clear from this graph that the price of one of the houses is badly fitted by the model: the actual price of house number 15 is nearly £3000 less than its fitted or expected price. The disparity of this house from the others was also reported in the summaries of the last two analyses. This may tell us that the house is a bargain; on the other hand perhaps it is in very bad condition or stands on the route of a new motorway. Like the prospective purchasers you should regard house number 15 with suspicion, since it does not seem to conform to the trends that are being investigated. You might change the value of Price for this house to 'missing' (*) and re-analyse the data. The house would be excluded from the new analysis.

4.6 Summary

Chapter 4 is concerned mainly with fitting linear regression models, though some other features of Genstat are introduced as well.

In order to fit a single regression model, the following statements are used:

MODEL   giving the response variate
FIT   providing a list of explanatory variates

In order to fit a sequence of regression models, an extra statement must be given before FIT:

TERMS   listing all variates to be used in the models

Then the set of explanatory variates in the model is defined or modified by:

FIT   providing a list of explanatory variates to define a model,
ADD   giving additional explanatory variates to add to the previous model,
DROP   saying which explanatory variates to drop from the previous model,
                  or
SWITCH   dropping some explanatory variates that are in the previous model and adding others that are not.

The constant may be dropped from the model — the regression line fitted through the origin — by setting the option CONSTANT=omit in any of these four statements.

Many Genstat statements have an option called PRINT to control the output. Each setting corresponds to a section of output. The PRINT option in the statements FIT, ADD, DROP and SWITCH can include the following words:

model   description of the model fitted,
summary   analysis of variance and percentage variance accounted for,

estimates   regression coefficients, and
fittedvalues   table of observed, fitted and residual values.

The option PRINT=correlations in the TERMS statement will produce a matrix of correlations between all the variates listed.

Two statements can be used to look at or save results from a fitted model:

RDISPLAY prints results, with a PRINT option as for FIT, and
RKEEP   saves results, with parameters RESIDUALS and FITTED-VALUES.

4.7 Exercises

4(1) An absorptiometer was used to measure the absorption of light passing through suspensions that contained different numbers of cells. It was intended to estimate the number of cells in future suspensions by the rapid light absorption method, so it was decided to regress cell counts on light absorption. The data are given below, where X is the absorptiometer reading and Y the cell count (10^8/ml).

X	Y	X	Y	X	Y
0.37	8.2	0.64	12.1	0.84	15.8
0.59	10.6	0.77	14.2	0.71	18.2
0.48	7.3	0.78	16.1	1.02	16.8
0.62	13.3	0.93	15.0	0.91	19.1
0.74	11.4	0.81	16.9	0.94	23.4
0.71	12.9				

(Example from *Experimentation in Biology*, Ridgman, 1975, Blackie, Glasgow.)

Arrange these data in a form appropriate for reading by Genstat, and write a program to regress cell count on absorptiometer reading. Produce a graphical display of the regression, giving a scatter plot of the observations and a line plot of the line of best fit.

4(2) A product is known to lose weight after manufacture. The following measurements were made (weights are in 1/16 oz):

Time after production	Weight difference
0.0	0.21
0.5	−1.46
1.0	−3.04
1.5	−3.21
2.0	−5.04
2.5	−5.37
3.0	−6.03
3.5	−7.21
4.0	−7.46
4.5	−7.96

(Example from *Applied Regression Analysis*, Draper & Smith, 1981, Wiley, New York.)

Fit a quadratic model that represents the loss of weight as a function of time: that is, a model with time and time^2 as the explanatory variables.

Look at the residuals from this model and draw conclusions about the validity of the model. This can be done by plotting residuals against fitted values, and residuals against time, for example.

In order to see what happens to the scatter plots when an inadequate model is fitted, remove the quadratic term from the model.

4(3) An attempt was made to predict the total mark of candidates in a school examination from their mark in the compulsory papers, together with their mark in an English language paper on a previous occasion. Some of the data obtained are presented below.

Candidate	Total mark (T)	Compulsory papers (C)	Previous paper (P)
1	476	111	68
2	457	92	46
3	540	90	50
4	551	107	59
5	575	98	50
6	698	150	66
7	545	118	54
8	574	110	51
9	645	117	59
10	556	94	97
11	634	130	57
12	637	118	51
13	390	91	44
14	562	118	61
15	560	109	66

(Example from *Applied Regression Analysis*, Draper & Smith, 1981, Wiley, New York.)

Write a Genstat program to regress T first on C, then on C and P together. The program should give results allowing you to test whether there is a significant improvement in prediction of T from including P in the model.

5 Language: 'Genstat as she is spoke'

5.1 Introduction

So far the Genstat instructions have been kept as simple as possible to introduce the concepts of the Genstat language without delay. However, some refinements of the language have been touched on, such as the abbreviation of the progression 1,2,3,4,5,6,7,8,9,10,11,12,13,14,15,16,17,18 to 1 ... 18 (Chapter 3, Section 3.2.4). More features like these, which reduce the length of your programs, are introduced in this chapter; also more information about doing calculations, and ways to deal with programming mistakes. We shall continue to introduce these features in the context of practical examples, but you will see programs that are more concise and efficient than before.

5.2 Writing compact programs

5.2.1 Grouping statements of the same type

The first example is about a technique called 'harmonic analysis' which is used for fitting a smooth, cyclical curve to a series of observations. We shall look at some data from the meat industry in the USA between 1919 and 1938: a series of monthly counts of slaughtered sheep, seasonally adjusted. The data are taken from *Statistics for Economics* (Greenwald, 1963, Merrill, Columbus) where it is shown that after the removal of a clear annual fluctuation in the numbers slaughtered, there remained a cyclical trend with a period of 20 months. Harmonic analysis reveals this trend by fitting to the data a function involving sines and cosines. Terms having periods of 20 months, 10 months, 5 months, and so on, can be included in the function. The inclusion of terms with shorter periodicity makes the function fit the data better, but at the cost of picking up the random fluctuations as well as the underlying cyclical trend.

All we need for the calculations are the averages for each month over the 12 available 20-month periods, expressed as percentages of the overall average, as follows:

Month	1	2	3	4	5	6	7
Average	98.7	99.1	93.2	97.8	100.2	97.5	101.3

Month	8	10	11	12	13	14	
Average	101.3	99.6	107.8	101.4	101.4	100.2	100.9

Month	15	16	17	18	19	20
Average	101.1	102.5	101.0	98.7	99.9	96.7

The harmonic function, H(*i*), of the series is defined by the expression

$$H(i) = a + b \times \sin\left(2\pi\,\frac{i}{20}\right) + c \times \cos\left(2\pi\,\frac{i}{20}\right)$$

where *i* varies from 1 up to 20. The coefficient *a* is simply the overall mean value of the series, which is 100%, whereas *b* is calculated from the averages in the table:

$$b = \frac{2}{20} \times \sum_{i=1}^{20}\left[\text{average}_i \times \sin\left(2\pi\,\frac{i}{20}\right)\right]$$

where average$_i$ is the average for the *i*th month. The coefficient *c* is derived from a similar expression using the cosine in place of the sine function.

Armed with these formulae it is possible to write a short Genstat program to calculate the harmonic function:

```
VARIATE [VALUES=1 ... 20] I
UNITS I
READ Average
(data):
SCALAR [VALUE=3.14159] Pi
CALCULATE X = 2 * Pi * I / 20
& B = 2 / 20 * SUM ( Average * SIN ( X ) )
& C = 2 / 20 * SUM ( Average * COS ( X ) )
& Harmonic = 100 + B * SIN ( X ) + C * COS ( X )
```

Several short cuts have been used in this program to save typing. Firstly, a UNITS statement has been used to save declaring the structure Average. In most Genstat commands that assign values to data structures, it is clear what type of data structure is needed, such as scalar or variate, and how many values it should have. However, the READ command can assign values to any type of structure, and you should specify the number of values so that the data can be checked for errors. If a structure is not declared, it is assumed in READ to be a variate and to have the number of values specified in the latest UNITS statement, if any. The number of values must be specified by one means or another or the program will fail.

The UNITS statement can also provide labels for the rows of the data matrix. Here the labels are only the numbers 1 to 20, but you will see more informative labels in

Section 5.3.1. You may want to specify a default length for READ without setting up any labels; if so, use a statement like this:

```
UNITS [NVALUES=20]
```

Another short cut is the use of the ampersand (&) as a repetition symbol to repeat the directive name used in the previous statement. Thus

```
CALCULATE X = 2 * Pi * I / 20
& B = 2 / 20 * SUM ( Average * SIN ( X ) )
```

is short for

```
CALCULATE X = 2 * Pi * I / 20
CALCULATE B = 2 / 20 * SUM ( Average * SIN ( X ) )
```

The structures B and C are not explicitly declared as scalars. Any structure that is given values within a CALCULATE statement will be set up automatically if it has not been already, and since it is clear here that the results of the calculations are single numbers, B and C are set up as scalars. It is often considered good programming practice, however, to declare all structures explicitly, particularly in large programs, because it provides an extra safeguard against typing errors.

Another piece of shorthand — the three dots in the VARIATE statement — can be used not only to represent a series of consecutive whole numbers (Chapter 3, Section 3.2.4) but to represent any arithmetic progression. For example the effects of the VARIATE statement and the first CALCULATE statement could be combined as follows:

```
VARIATE [VALUES=0.314159, 0.628318 ... 6.28318] X
```

Note that if the progression does not increase, or decrease, by one at a time, the second element must be given as well as the first and last.

5.2.2 Standard functions

The calculations are reproduced in the program just as they appear in the text above, except that the expression $2\pi i/20$ has been calculated first, which improves computational efficiency since it is required in both expressions. The items SIN and COS are standard names of *functions* in the Genstat language and are included in CALCULATE statements with a pair of brackets enclosing the *argument* of the function. Here X is a variate with 20 values, so SIN(X) will work out 20 sines. SUM is another standard function, which adds up the values in the argument to give a scalar result. For example,

```
VARIATE [VALUES=3,4,5] Z
CALCULATE S = SUM(Z)
```

gives the value 12 to the scalar S.

Here are some other functions:

like SIN and COS:
SQRT	square root,
LOG	natural logarithm,
LOG10	logarithm to base 10 and
EXP	exponential;

like SUM: MEAN, MINIMUM, MAXIMUM, VARIANCE, and MEDIAN.

The functions SIN and COS are used again in the last CALCULATE statement where each of the 20 values they produce is used to calculate one value of the variate Harmonic.

The harmonic function can be illustrated with a GRAPH statement:

```
 1  VARIATE[VALUES=1...20]I
 2  UNITS I
 3  READ Average
```

Identifier	Minimum	Mean	Maximum	Values	Missing
Average	93.2	100.0	107.8	20	0

```
 7  SCALAR[VALUE=3.14159]Pi
 8  CALCULATE X = 2*Pi*I/20
 9  & B = 2 / 20 * SUM ( Average * SIN ( X ) )
10  & C = 2 / 20 * SUM ( Average * COS ( X ) )
11  & Harmonic = 100 + B * SIN ( X ) + C * COS ( X )
12  GRAPH[YTITLE='Percent';XTITLE='MONTHS';\
13     NROWS=21;NCOLUMNS=61]Y=Harmonic,Average;X=I;\
14     METHOD=curve,line;SYMBOL='.','*'
```

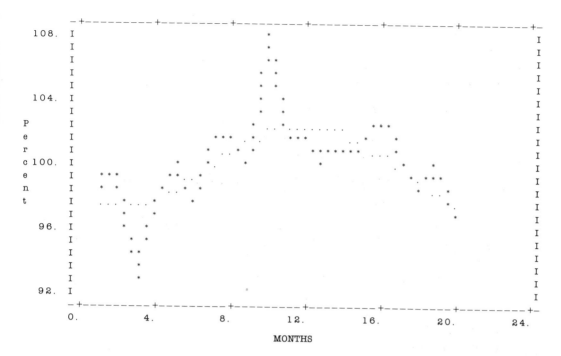

5.2.3 Combining statements that do similar things

The above graph shows that although simple harmonic analysis smoothes the erratic jumps, it misses quite a lot of the pattern that is evident in the data. For example, the maximum of the harmonic appears between the maximum of the observations at month 10 and the next peak at month 16. This seems unacceptable. An improvement on the curve can be made by using a multiple harmonic wave which is the sum of two harmonic curves and will follow the observations more closely. The calculations needed for the second harmonic are almost the same as for the first, the only difference being that the periodicity is halved; that is, SIN (X * 2) replaces SIN (X) and COS (X * 2) replaces COS (X).

We cannot use the same scalars B and C for both harmonics, so we shall use the pairs of identifiers B[1], C[1] and B[2], C[2] to distinguish the two curves. In Genstat any identifier can include a numerical suffix in square brackets and this is treated as part of the identifier:

```
SCALAR B[1], B[2], C[1], C[2]
```

We shall similarly use two variates called Harmonic[1] and Harmonic[2] to store the points on the two curves. It is important to note that we cannot use these suffixed identifiers in the same program as we use the unsuffixed identifiers B, C, and Harmonic. This is because Genstat treats a suffixed identifier as the value of a special structure called a *pointer*, that is designed to store a series of identifiers. As soon as the suffixed identifiers B[1] and B[2] are referred to, Genstat automatically sets up a pointer structure that points to the two scalars. You could declare this pointer explicitly:

```
POINTER [NVALUES=2] B
```

but it is not necessary. Of course, the identifier B cannot stand at the same time for a scalar and a pointer in the same program; B[1], though, can be a completely different type of structure to B[2].

Rather than give two more statements to calculate the coefficients of the second harmonic, we can extend the statements from the last section:

```
SCALAR B[1], B[2], C[1], C[2]
CALCULATE B[1], B[2] = 2 / 20 * SUM(Average * SIN(X*1,2))
&          C[1], C[2] = 2 / 20 * SUM(Average * COS(X*1,2))
& Harmonic[1], Harmonic[2] = 100 + B[1], B[2] * SIN(X*1,2)
                                 + C[1], C[2] * COS(X*1,2)
```

The first CALCULATE statement is equivalent to (but more efficient than) two separate statements:

```
CALCULATE B[1] = 2 / 20 * SUM(Average * SIN(X*1))
&         B[2] = 2 / 20 * SUM(Average * SIN(X*2))
```

Thus any multiple calculations can be done in Genstat by replacing single identifiers by lists of identifiers that are matched up throughout the expression. In fact the statements above can be made even shorter since the identifiers have suffixes. B[1], B[2] can be replaced by B[1,2], and so on; thus the statements become:

```
SCALAR B[1,2], C[1,2]
CALCULATE B[1,2] = 2 / 20 * SUM(Average * SIN(X*1,2))
&         C[1,2] = 2 / 20 * SUM(Average * COS(X*1,2))
& Harmonic[1,2] = 100 + B[1,2] * SIN(X*1,2) + C[1,2] * COS(X*1,2)
```

The multiple harmonic is the sum of the harmonics that have been calculated, adjusted so that the mean is still 100:

```
CALCULATE Multiple = Harmonic[1] + Harmonic[2] — 100
GRAPH [YTITLE='Percent'; XTITLE='M O N T H S'] \
    Y=Multiple,Average; X=I; METHOD=curve,line; SYMBOL='.','*'
```

The listing of the final program and the new graph are shown below:

```
 1  VARIATE[VALUES=1...20]I
 2  UNITS I
 3  READ Average
```

Identifier	Minimum	Mean	Maximum	Values	Missing
Average	93.2	100.0	107.8	20	0

```
 7  SCALAR B[1,2],C[1,2]&[VALUE=3.14159]Pi
 8  CALCULATE X = 2 * Pi * I / 20
 9  & B[1,2] = 2 / 20 * SUM(Average * SIN(X*1,2))
10  & C[1,2] = 2 / 20 * SUM(Average * COS(X*1,2))
11  & Harmonic[1,2] = 100 + B[1,2] * SIN(X*1,2) + C[1,2] * COS(X*1,2)
12  & Multiple = Harmonic[1] + Harmonic[2] — 100
13  GRAPH[YTITLE='Percent'; XTITLE='MONTHS'; \
14      NROWS=21; NCOLUMNS=61]Y=Harmonic[1],Average; X=I; \
15      METHOD=curve,line; SYMBOL='.','*'
16  &Y=Multiple,Average; X=I; METHOD=curve,line; SYMBOL='.','*'
```

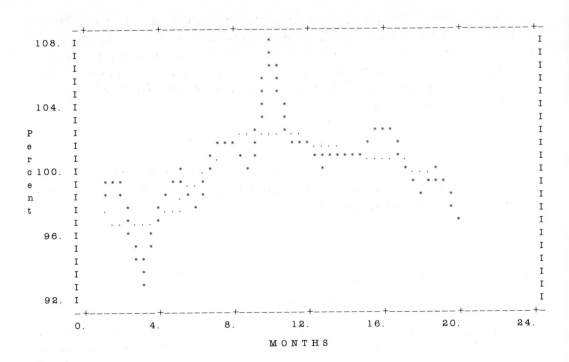

From the graph you can see that the multiple harmonic follows the data more closely than the simple harmonic.

The calculations in the program have been made a little more compact and some of the statements have been reordered to put statements of the same kind together. With some types of computer this gives greater computational efficiency and it always allows you to make more use of the ampersand to reduce typing. Notice that ampersand, as used in the two GRAPH statements, stands for a repeat of all option settings as well as of the directive name. However, if it had been necessary to modify the option settings, new settings could have been given in square brackets as usual, after the ampersand. It is important to note that any options that are not reset remain as in the first statement. Thus in the following statements

```
GRAPH [TITLE='First order'; YTITLE='Percent'; XTITLE='M O N T H S']\
    Y=Harmonic[1], Average; X=I;\
    METHOD=curve,line; SYMBOL='.','*'
& [TITLE='Second order'] Y=Multiple, Average; X=I;\
    METHOD=curve,line; SYMBOL='.','*'
```

the second graph too has titles printed on the x-axis and y-axis.

We have also put the two statements declaring scalars together on one line. There is complete freedom to do this in Genstat, because it is quite clear when an ampersand is met, that the first statement is finished and another is starting. In fact, any number of statements of any type may be put on the same line. If one statement is followed by another and ampersand is not used, then the colon (:) must be used to show the end of the first statement:

```
VARIATE [VALUES=1...20] I: UNITS I: READ Average
```

The colon can thus be used to terminate statements as well as data. We recommend that you keep statements on separate lines in general, because it makes programs easier to read and understand.

5.3 Abbreviating individual statements

5.3.1 Reading data from a separate data file

The next example concerns natural evaporation from areas of open water, bare soil or grassland — a variable which is difficult to measure but which can be estimated by means of a standard formula (*Natural evaporation from open water, bare soil and grass*, Penman, 1948, Proceedings of the Royal Society A 193, 120-145). We shall apply this formula to data from English grassland in 1963 to estimate the average daily evaporation rate during each month of that year. The formula itself is complex; we shall not attempt to describe the basis of it nor the derivation of the values given to the various constants for this set of data. The point of the example is to show a practical application of Genstat and to illustrate some useful programming features.

The data needed for the formula are as follows:

a) radiation: measured as the equivalent number of mm of water that the total energy could evaporate,
b) proportion of daytime with sunshine,
c) temperature (°K),
d) saturation vapour pressure (mm Hg) and
e) wind speed in 100 miles/day.

The values of these variables for each month of 1963 are available and indexed by the name of the month, but they are recorded using more conventional physical units. The radiation is in calories/cm^2/day, temperature is in °C, vapour pressure is in millibars and wind speed in km/day. The data are already in a file in the computer, arranged as follows:

January	54	0.24	−3.3	4.3	229
February	108	0.25	−2.0	4.7	221
March	163	0.23	5.5	7.5	267
April	253	0.28	8.4	9.1	220
May	369	0.39	10.2	9.4	259
June	392	0.37	14.4	12.9	212
July	385	0.38	14.8	13.9	137
August	271	0.26	14.1	13.1	193
September	228	0.33	12.9	12.1	179
October	122	0.22	10.3	11.0	182
November	63	0.17	7.6	9.4	238
December	42	0.17	1.3	6.1	246 :

It is easier to read the data from the data file rather than copy the values into the program. To do this, a second channel for information to go to Genstat must be opened, and the file must be attached to it, as described in Chapter 2. This is done by the statement:

```
OPEN 'Penman.dat'; CHANNEL=2
```

assuming Penman.dat is the name of the file. The data are then read from the file by means of the following Genstat statements:

```
TEXT [NVALUES=12] Month
UNITS Month
READ [CHANNEL=2] Month, Radiation, Sunhours, Temperature, Svp, Speed
```

The option [CHANNEL=2] in the READ statement indicates that the data are to be read from the second channel: without this option, they would be expected to follow the READ statement as in previous examples.

The structure Month is included to store the labels that index the data. Since the names of the months are not numbers, they are stored in a TEXT structure. The length of this structure — the number of textual strings — is used to define the default length of the variates by including a UNITS statement. A string in the Genstat language was defined in Section 3.3.2 to be any sequence of characters inside single quotes or any sequence of letters and numbers starting with a letter. Thus January21st and 'January 21st' are strings but January 21st is not. Certainly the months January, February, and so on are valid strings.

5.3.2 Abbreviating directive names, options, and parameters

Before looking at the data, we can transform them into the correct units for the formula:

```
CALC Radiation = Radiation / 59
& Temperature = Temperature + 273
& Svp = 760 * Svp / 1013
& Speed = Speed / 160.93
PRINT Month, Radiation, Sunhours, Temperature, Svp, Speed;\
    DECIMALS=(0,2(2))2
```

The directive name CALCULATE has been abbreviated in the first statement. The rule in Genstat is that only the first four characters of a directive name are essential, so that CALC, CALCUL, or CALCULATE are all acceptable. But it does make programs less readable when abbreviations are used: we shall continue to give the full directive names in the examples. If you misspell directive names, it will matter only if the misspelling occurs in the first eight letters. Thus CALCULATR will be accepted whereas CALCULARE will not.

Option and parameter names may also be abbreviated. The rule for such a name is that only as many letters need be given as distinguish the name from all previous names of the same type in the statement. Thus the following two statements are identical:

```
GRAPH [TITLE='Penman'; YTITLE='Radiation'] Y=Radiation; X=Month
GRAPH [T='Penman'; Y='Radiation'] Y=Radiation; X=Month
```

Usually the shortest form is a single letter, but in statements with many options, like GRAPH, some of the less often used ones (defined last in the statement) may need two, three, or even four letters. For example, you have seen the options YLOWER, YUPPER of GRAPH in Chapter 3, and their shortest forms are YL and YU.

Options and parameters can be put in any statement without their names so long as they are in correct order. Thus the following statement is equivalent to the preceding one:

```
GRAPH [; 'Penman'; 'Radiation'] Radiation; Month
```

The first option of GRAPH is a CHANNEL option, not set explicitly in this statement, to allow graphs to be sent to alternative output files (in the same way as CHANNEL in READ allows data to be read from different input files). TITLE and YTITLE are the second and third options respectively. Similarly, Y and X are the first and second parameters of GRAPH.

The order of options and parameters is given in the *Genstat 5 Reference Manual* (Payne, Lane *et al*, 1987, Oxford University Press). The order can also be checked by giving a HELP statement within Genstat: this statement is analogous to the HELP statement available within most computer operating systems to give information about operating-system commands (Chapter 2, Section 2.2). For example, to get information about the options of GRAPH when running Genstat interactively, type

```
HELP graph,options
```

If you try using the HELP statement you will find out how to use it to get any of the information it can provide.

Leaving off the name can be convenient for a common first parameter like Y in GRAPH; but since you have to memorize the correct order, or look it up, we do not recommend it as a general practice. If you include the names you can put the options and parameters in any order without ambiguity; thus the following statement is also equivalent to the preceding one:

```
GRAPH [YTITLE='Radiation'; TITLE='Penman'] X=Month; Y=Radiation
```

5.3.3 Repetitive lists of numbers

Another abbreviation in the PRINT statement was the use of bracketed terms in the DECIMALS parameter:

```
DECIMALS=(0,2(2))2
```

The expression 2(2) is the same as 2,2. The 2 in front of the brackets is called a pre-multiplier and has the effect of repeating each item inside the brackets individually. Thus 3(1,5,6) is the same as 1,1,1,5,5,5,6,6,6. Similarly the last 2 in the PRINT statement is a post-multiplier which has the effect of repeating a whole sequence of numbers. Thus (1,5,6)3 is the same as 1,5,6,1,5,6,1,5,6. Hence the DECIMALS parameter setting above is equivalent to 0,2,2,0,2,2 which specifies the number of decimals for printing each of the six structures in the statement. The number 0 corresponding to the text structure will be ignored, since the values are not numerical. Long lists can be built up compactly using these multipliers: 3(1...4)2 is the same as 1,1,1,2,2,2,3,3,3,4,4,4,1,1,1,2,2,2,3,3,3,4,4,4.

5.3.4 Abbreviating identifiers

The results of the PRINT statement are shown in the output that is produced by the statements so far:

```
1   OPEN'Penman.dat';CHANNEL=2
2   TEXT[NVALUES=12]Month
3   UNITS Month
4   READ[CHANNEL=2] Month, Radiation, Sunhours, Temperature,\
5       Svp, Speed
```

Identifier	Minimum	Mean	Maximum	Values	Missing
Radiatio	42.0	204.2	392.0	12	0
Sunhours	0.1700	0.2742	0.3900	12	0
Temperat	−3.300	7.850	14.800	12	0
Svp	4.300	9.458	13.900	12	0
Speed	137.0	215.3	267.0	12	0

```
6   CALC Radiation = Radiation / 59
7   & Temperature = Temperature + 273
8   & Svp = 760 * Svp / 1013
9   & Speed = Speed / 160.93
10  PRINT Month, Radiation, Sunhours, Temperature, Svp, Speed;\
11      DECIMALS=(0,2(2))2
```

Month	Radiatio	Sunhours	Temperat	Svp	Speed
January	0.92	0.24	270	3.23	1.42
February	1.83	0.25	271	3.53	1.37
March	2.76	0.23	279	5.63	1.66
April	4.29	0.28	281	6.83	1.37
May	6.25	0.39	283	7.05	1.61
June	6.64	0.37	287	9.68	1.32
July	6.53	0.38	288	10.43	0.85
August	4.59	0.26	287	9.83	1.20
September	3.86	0.33	286	9.08	1.11
October	2.07	0.22	283	8.25	1.13
November	1.07	0.17	281	7.05	1.48
December	0.71	0.17	274	4.58	1.53

In the table of data, some variate identifiers have been curtailed: 'Radiatio' for Radiation and 'Temperat' for Temperature. This is because only the first eight characters of an identifier are stored. It is important to realize that identifiers such as Yield1986 and Yield1987 are therefore treated as being the same and refer to the same structure since they differ only in the ninth character. Suffixes should be used in cases like this; thus Yield[1986] and Yield[1987] are completely separate identifiers. To avoid making mistakes, we recommend you use up to eight characters only for identifiers, as we do in the other examples in this book.

5.3.5 Exponent notation for numbers

Returning to the example, we are now in a position to use Penman's formula to estimate the natural evaporation rate. This is done by four CALCULATE statements that derive the net radiation and the evaporation rate using two temporary variates, Temp1 and Temp2, for convenience:

```
CALCULATE Netrad = Radiation*0.75—(0.47-0.075*SQRT(Svp))*
   (2.03E—9*Temperature**4)*(0.17+0.83*Sunhours)
& Temp1 = EXP(47.226—6463/Temperature—3.927*LOG(Temperature))
& Temp2 = Temp1*(6463/Temperature—3.972)/Temperature/0.486
& Evaporat = (Netrad*Temp2+0.35*(Temp1—Svp)*(1+Speed))/(1+Temp2)
```

Three standard functions have been used in these expressions: SQRT for square root, EXP for exponential and LOG for natural logarithm. (If you want to use logarithms to the base 10, the function name is LOG10.) Apart from these functions, the calculations involve only the basic arithmetic operations applied to the variates we derived, and several constants that occur in Penman's formula. Notice, however, that one of these constants is represented in exponent notation: '2.03E-9' in the second line is the same as 0.00000000203 (see Chapter 4, Section 4.3.2).

Finally the results are printed, followed by a short description:

```
12  CALCULATE  Netrad=Radiation*0.75-(0.47-0.075*SQRT(Svp))*\
13     (2.03E—9*Temperature**4)*(0.17+0.83*Sunhours)
14  &Temp1=EXP(47.226-6463/Temperature—3.927*LOG(Temperature))
15  & Temp2=Temp1*(6463/Temperature—3.972)/Temperature/0.486
16  &Evaporat=(Netrad*Temp2+0.35*(Temp1-Svp)*(1+Speed))/(1+Temp
17  PRINT  Month,Netrad,Evaporat;DECIMALS=3
```

Month	Netrad	Evaporat
January	—0.643	—0.022
February	0.012	0.233
March	0.785	0.928
April	1.812	1.521
May	2.945	2.561
June	3.419	2.921
July	3.354	2.624

August	2.195	2.007
September	1.429	1.467
October	0.377	0.581
November	—0.259	0.184
December	—0.573	—0.009

```
18   "Monthly evaporation in 1963:
-19  Net radiation in mm/day, Evaporation rate in mm/day"
```

Note that a *comment*, delimited by double quotes, can be included anywhere in a Genstat program. Its only purpose is to provide information to someone reading the program, or the copy of the program included in the output file: Genstat ignores the comment, except to print a minus sign against the line number of any line that starts as a comment (it also does this if the line starts as a quoted string). The minus signs make it easy to see when a quote has been forgotten.

5.4 Diagnosing mistakes in programs

5.4.1 The problem of mistakes

The preparation of programs for a computer provides plenty of scope for making mistakes even when small jobs are attempted. In Genstat, as in all other computer languages, large programs rarely work first time. It is therefore important that Genstat should not only execute statements that are right but should give helpful error messages when it finds wrong ones.

There is a limit to the amount of help that Genstat will give. For example, it can tell you that you are asking it to do calculations on variates whose values have never been set. But it is up to you to spot whether you forgot to calculate these values 20 lines earlier, or whether the 'new' variate is actually an existing one with its identifier misspelled.

If there is anything wrong with the output from your Genstat program, you should first try to decide where the fault lies: in the Genstat statements, or in the instructions controlling the running of your program that are local to your computer. If the control instructions are at fault, you may need to ask your computer advisory service. You can tell if the Genstat statements themselves are at fault, because all error messages produced by Genstat have a characteristic form.

5.4.2 Syntax errors

Consider the following statement:

```
PRlNT Month,Netrad,Evaporat; DECIMALS=3
```

If this were included in the program discussed in Section 5.3, Genstat would not produce the results but would print a message instead:

```
******** Fault (Code SX 4). Statement 1 on Line 16
At... PRlN\T\ Month,Net
SX 4 Unknown directive name
```

The 16 corresponds to a line number printed with the copy of the program, and the statement number indicates the actual statement involved, because there may be several statements on the line. The code 'SX 4' (SX stands for SyntaX) can be looked up in the *Genstat 5 Reference Manual* to find further explanation if the message on the next line is not sufficient. Together with the copy of the statement with backslashes showing where the offending item is, the message makes it clear what has happened: the digit 1 has been used instead of the letter I in PRINT.

What is a syntax error? Consider an instruction written in English, such as 'Put the kettle on the stove'. There are several kinds of mistake that could be made in the instruction, making it impossible to obey. Firstly, you might be told 'The put kettle on the stove' which is simply incorrect English. Secondly, you might be told 'Put the generosity on the stove' which is correct English but a meaningless instruction. Thirdly, you might be told 'Put the kettle on the stove' but there might be some objection such as 'There is no stove'. A syntax error is an error of the first kind and is detected when you try to read the instruction. Errors of the second kind will be detected when you try to understand the instruction; errors of the third kind only when you try to obey it.

5.4.3 Meaningless statements

Here is an example of the second kind of error, where a statement has correct syntax but is actually meaningless:

```
1  VARIATE[NVALUES=4;VALUES=0...4]Integer

******** Fault (Code VA 13). Statement 1 on Line 1
Command: VARIATE[NVALUES=4;VALUES=0...4]Integer

Invalid or incompatible numbers of values
Structure has 5 values, whereas it should have 4.
```

The message is clear here: there are five integers in the progression 0,1,2,3,4 and not four. Syntactically the statement is correct since it is possible to set the length of a structure and give it values at the same time. But it is meaningless when there is a contradiction between the length and the number of values.

Many errors of the second kind are not found until a later statement, correct in itself, is executed:

```
 9  VARIATE[VALUES=1,1.2...10.4]X
10  &[VALUES=9.3,9...−5.1]Y
11  CALCULATE  S=SUM(X*Y)

******** Fault (Code VA 13). Statement 1 on Line 11
Command:CALCULATE  S=SUM(X*Y)

Invalid or incompatible numbers of values
Structure Y has 49 values, whereas it should have 48.
```

X cannot be multiplied by Y: X has 48 values and Y has 49, so their values do not correspond. Again the message makes the problem easy to diagnose. The message is printed after the CALCULATE statement, but it is probably line 9 or 10 that needs to be amended.

5.4.4 Unexecutable statements

The third kind of error occurs when an instruction is sensible but cannot be obeyed for some reason. For example:

```
1  UNIT[NVALUES=20]
2  OPEN'Recovery.dat';CHANNEL=2
3  READ[CHANNEL=2; PRINT=*]Recovery,Dose,Duration,Age,Pressure
4  FIT Dose,Duration

******** Fault (Code RE 10). Statement 1 on Line 4
Command: FIT Dose,Duration

Regression models cannot be fitted until a MODEL statement is given
```

It is clear that a regression analysis is required for the two explanatory variates Dose and Duration, but no MODEL statement has been given to specify which of the other three variates is to be the response variate in the analysis.

5.5 Summary

Chapter 5 describes ways to make Genstat programs short to reduce the chance of making mistakes, and how to deal with mistakes when they do occur.

The following shorthand methods can be used.

a)   The ampersand (&) is used to repeat a directive name, plus options if appropriate.

b)   Arithmetic progressions may be represented concisely using three dots (...).

c)   Repetitive lists of numbers may be written compactly with pre- and post-multipliers.

d)   Most items in a program may be shortened if necessary: directive names have four essential characters, identifiers have up to eight.

e)   Option and parameter names may be omitted if the settings are in the right order.

f)   Identifiers may have numerical suffixes in brackets which are treated as part of the identifier; lists of suffixed identifiers may be contracted using suffix lists.

Calculations can be made concise as follows.

a)   Calculations that do similar things may be combined in a single statement using lists of identifiers.

b)   Standard functions are provided in the CALCULATE statement.

c)   Individual numbers may be written in exponent notation if convenient.

A structure can be defined to label the rows of the data matrix by a statement of the form:

```
UNITS [NVALUES=number] variate or text
```

The length of the units structure is taken as the default length of variates and texts by READ.

The HELP statement provides information about Genstat.

Mistakes in Genstat statements are classified into:

a)   syntax errors, noticed when statements are read,

b)   meaningless statements, noticed when Genstat tries to understand them, and

c)   unexecutable statements, noticed only when Genstat tries to obey them.

Genstat prints a short descriptive message about each mistake it finds.

5.6 Exercises

5(1) The following program has been written correctly to produce two regression analyses of a set of data:

```
VARIATE [NVALUES=27] X,Y,T
TEXT Ht; VALUES='TIME': READ [SERIAL=no] X,Y,T
    1    0   21    2    2   25    3    4   29    4    7   33    5    8   37
    6   10   41    7   12   45    8   15   49    9   16   53   10   19   57
   11   21   61   12   24   65   13   25   69   14   28   73   15   31   77
   16   32   81   17   35   85   18   38   89   19   40   93   20   42   97
   21   44  101   22   47  105   23   49  109   24   51  113   25   54  117
   26   57  121   27   59  125   :
VARIATE [NVALUES=27] Logy: CALCULATE Logy = LOG(0.35+Y)
MODEL Logy
VARIATE [NVALUES=27] R: FIT [PRINT=model,summary,estimate] X
RKEEP RESIDUALS=R
TEXT Hy; VALUES='Residuals': GRAPH [YTITLE=Hy; XTITLE=Ht] Y=R; X=T
SCALAR M: CALCULATE M = MEAN(X)
VARIATE [NVALUES=27] X2: CALCULATE X2 = (X—M) * (X—M)
MODEL Logy
VARIATE [NVALUES=27] S: FIT X,X2
RKEEP RESIDUALS=S
GRAPH [XTITLE=Ht; YTITLE=Hy] Y=S; X=T
STOP
```

The statements appear in the order in which they occurred to the programmer. The program is inefficient in the following ways:

a) an unnecessarily large amount of material must be presented to the computer, involving more typing work and more possibility of error;

b) storage space has been wasted by using unnecessary data structures; and

c) there is no attempt to group together each type of operation employed, such as calculation, drawing graphs, regression analysis, which could save time on many types of computer.

Rewrite the program to make it more efficient in these terms, but still as easy as possible to read and understand.

Rewrite the program again to be as compact as possible, but with the output still labelled as in the original; for example, leave the identifier of the response variate as Logy. Including necessary spaces and newlines, 236 characters are sufficient. But to achieve this you would need to use the HELP statement to find the most concise form of options and parameters.

5(2) Explain the diagnostics shown in the following piece of output.

```
1   VARIATE[NVALUES=8]Volume,Mass,Conc
2   &[NVALUES=8]Time;VALUES=0...8
```

```
******** Warning (Code SX 49). Statement 1 on Line 2
At...LUES=0...8 \:\
First parameter list not longest: extra elements will be ignored
```

```
******** Fault (Code VA 13). Statement 1 on Line 2
Command: &[NVALUES=8]Time;VALUES=0...8
```

```
Invalid or incompatible numbers of values
Structure has 1 value, whereas it should have 8.
```

```
3   READ[SERIAL=not]Volume,Mass
```

```
******** Fault (Code SX 6). Statement 1 on Line 3
At...SERIAL=not \]\ Volume,Ma
Invalid option value
```

```
4   10 12 25 27 28 30 41 43 :
```

```
******** Fault (Code SX 10). Statement 1 on Line 4
At...\ 10 12 25 2
Invalid character in element
```

```
5   4.3 5.6 6.2 5.6 8.3 6.5 7.8 8.2 :
```

```
******** Fault (Code SX 10). Statement 1 on Line 5
At... \ 4.3 5.6 6.
Invalid character in element
```

```
6   CALCULATE  Conc=(1.25+Mass)/Volume)*100
```

```
******** Fault (Code SX 13). Statement 1 on Line 6
At... s)/Volume)\*\ 100:
Syntactic error (e.g. unmatched brackets)
```

```
7   TEXT  Time;VALUES=Time(hours)
```

```
******** Fault (Code SX 12). Statement 1 on Line 7
At...LUES=Time\(\hours):
Incompatible adjacent elements (e.g. comma missing)
```

```
8  & Conc; VALUES = 'Concentration (mg/litre)'
```

```
******** Fault (Code SX 2). Statement 1 on Line 8
At...  &  Conc; VAL
'&' invalid — no previous directive has been established
```

```
9  GRAPH[YTITLE = Conc; TTITLE = Time]Conc; Time
```

```
******** Fault (Code SX 5). Statement 1 on Line 9
At...nc; TTITLE \ = \ Time]Conc
Unknown option or parameter name
```

Can you find further faults in the program, which have not yet been detected by Genstat?

5(3) For eight weeks during the summer, a light-trap is used to catch moths at night-time. Data records have been prepared for each week, giving the number of moths belonging to each of 10 species that are captured:

```
 4   2   0    5    1   0   1    0   0   0
 8   0   0    9    1   0   3    0   1   0
12   1   0   12    2   2   3    0   4   0
19   3   0   26    4   1   2    0   3   1
24   5   0   21    9   3   4    3   2   0
28   0   0   15   13   2   6   11   0   1
31   2   0    5    4   0   7   25   3   0
35   1   0    1    1   1   5   43   0   0
```

Write a program to read these values in series into eight variates. Calculate and display the cumulative totals for each species at the end of each week, expressed as a percentage of the total numbers of moths of each species captured in the full period. You can write your program compactly if you use suffixes in the identifiers of data structures.

Can you carry out all the calculations with just two CALCULATE statements? Do not worry about the zero total for the third species: Genstat will avoid dividing by zero and will print a missing value automatically.

Write further statements to read the data values in parallel into 10 variates and do the same calculations. You will need a function that has not been introduced: CUMULATE gives cumulative values; for example,

```
VARIATE [VALUES=1,3,4] X
CALCULATE Y = CUMULATE(X)
```

gives the values 1, 4, 8 to the variate Y.

6 Tabulation

6.1 Introduction

As was shown in Chapter 3, graphs provide one method of emphasizing the salient features of data. When data are classified into groups, tables provide another method of summarizing the data, presenting quantitative information rather than the mostly qualitative information of graphs. Tables are useful for comparing numerical characteristics of the groups.

Before tables can be formed from data, the groups must first be defined. In Genstat, this is done using a data structure called a factor.

6.2 Forming two-way tables

6.2.1 Classifying data by factors

An experiment using 36 samples of Portland cement is described in *Statistical methods in research and production* (Davies, 1947, Oliver & Boyd, London). The samples were 'gauged' (mixed with water and worked) by three gaugers, each one gauging 12 samples. After the samples had set, the compressive strength was tested by three breakers, each breaker testing four samples from each of the three gaugers. So the samples are grouped in two ways — three groups for the gaugers and three groups for the breakers giving nine sub-groups in all, each sub-group containing four samples. The data are shown below. The measurement of Strength for one of the samples treated by Gauger 1 and Breaker 3 has been replaced by a missing value, as if the measurement were not available, to show how Genstat deals with missing values.

Sample	Gauger	Breaker	Strength
1	3	3	56.0
2	2	3	41.8
3	1	2	50.2
4	1	3	53.2
5	3	2	55.6
6	3	1	53.6
7	3	2	57.2
8	3	1	55.0
9	2	2	53.4
10	2	1	44.2
11	1	1	58.0
12	2	1	52.8
13	1	2	43.4

14	1	3	*
15	1	1	47.6
16	1	1	52.8
17	1	2	62.0
18	2	3	44.8
19	3	2	47.6
20	2	2	62.0
21	2	1	55.8
22	1	3	51.8
23	2	2	49.6
24	3	3	44.6
25	3	1	61.6
26	2	3	48.0
27	1	3	41.6
28	2	2	48.8
29	3	3	46.8
30	3	3	49.3
31	1	1	55.2
32	2	1	49.0
33	2	3	46.0
34	3	2	56.2
35	1	2	44.0
36	3	1	43.2

The data are arranged in a data matrix with 36 rows and four columns (see Chapter 1, Section 1.2.1). The first column contains the sample labels 1 to 36; as you have seen (Chapter 5, Section 5.2.1), such labels can be held in a structure declared in a UNITS statement. The last column holds the compressive strengths which may be any number within the range of possible strengths. Such values are held in a variate (Chapter 1, Section 1.2.1).

The numbers in the second and third columns specify the way in which the units of data are grouped. Each number can be only 1, 2, or 3 indicating which gauger and which breaker dealt with the corresponding sample. In Genstat such group numbers are held in structures called *factors*. Thus, two factors must be declared, each with three *levels* and 36 values. The levels of a factor are the possible numerical values: 1, 2 or 3 here. The following statements declare the factors, called Gauger and Breaker:

```
FACTOR [NVALUES=36; LEVELS=3] Gauger & Breaker
```

Like variates, factors are one-dimensional structures. As these two factors have the same numbers of levels and of values they can be specified using one statement only. Moreover, if a UNITS statement already specifies the standard length of one-dimensional structures as 36, it is not necessary to specify the number of values when declaring the factors. The two statements above can then be replaced by:

UNITS [NVALUES=36] Sample FACTOR [LEVELS=3] Gauger,Breaker

6.2.2 Forming tables of totals, with or without margins

If, for each sample, the compressive strengths are read into a variate called Strength then the values of Strength classified by the values of Gauger and Breaker can be tabulated. The TABULATE statement does this:

TABULATE [PRINT=totals; CLASSIFICATION=Gauger,Breaker] Strength

This statement specifies the variate whose values are to be summarized (Strength), what type of summaries are to be printed (totals), and which factors are to classify the summaries (Gauger and Breaker). The program so far and its output are shown below.

```
1   UNITS[NVALUES=36]Sample
2   FACTOR[LEVELS=3]Gauger,Breaker
3   READ Sample,Gauger,Breaker,Strength
```

Identifier	Minimum	Mean	Maximum	Values	Missing
Sample	1.00	18.50	36.00	36	0
Strength	41.60	50.93	62.00	36	1

```
12   TABULATE[PRINT=totals;CLASSIFICATION=Gauger,Breaker]Strength
```

	Total		
Breaker	1	2	3
Gauger			
1	213.6	199.6	146.6
2	201.8	213.8	180.6
3	213.4	216.6	196.7

Note that the values of the factors Gauger and Breaker can be read. (So far the READ statement has been used only with variates.) However, the summary of the data produced by the READ statement gives information only about the variates Sample and Strength. (Sample has not been defined explicitly, so is assumed to be a variate by Genstat.) It would not be very sensible to print the minimum, mean, and maximum values of the factors Gauger and Breaker as both structures have only three possible values, which are 1 or 2 or 3.

The table printed above has no margins; that is, there are no summaries of Strength for each gauger, combined over all breakers, nor for each breaker combined over all gaugers. The meaning of the term 'margin' is illustrated in the schematic table in Figure 6.1.

GAUGER	BREAKER	1	2	3	MARGIN
1		a	b	c	
2		d	e	f	
3		g	h	i	
MARGIN					

Figure 6.1: Schematic table including margins

To obtain margins, set an option in the TABULATE statement, thus:

```
TABULATE [PRINT=totals; CLASSIFICATION=Gauger,Breaker;\
    MARGINS=yes] Strength
```

The TABULATE statement with the MARGINS option at its default setting (MARGINS=no for no margins) sets up a table with the $3 \times 3 = 9$ cells (one for each subgroup) that are labelled a,b,c,d,e,f,g,h,i in the diagram. With the option set to give margins (MARGINS=yes), the TABULATE statement sets up a table which also contains the extra row and column labelled MARGIN in the diagram. This table has $(3+1) \times (3+1) = 16$ cells. The extra, marginal cells are given the row totals and column totals. The new version of the table, with margins, is shown below.

```
Breaker      1       2       3     Total
Gauger
     1     213.6   199.6   146.6    559.8
     2     201.8   213.8   180.6    596.2
     3     213.4   216.6   196.7    626.7
 Total     628.8   630.0   523.9   1782.7
```

6.2.3 Forming tables of counts and means

Here a table of totals is misleading, as all the totals are not based on the same number of samples. So a more useful summary is a table of means of the strengths in each classification. Such a summary can be formed with TABULATE by setting 'means' in the PRINT option in place of 'totals'. Other summaries can also be formed: we show below a table of the number of observations in each classification as well as the means.

```
15   TABULATE[PRINT=nobservations,means;
16      CLASSIFICATION=Gauger,Breaker;MARGINS=yes]Strength
```

Breaker	1		2	
	Nobservd	Mean	Nobservd	Mean
Gauger				
1	4	53.40	4	49.90
2	4	50.45	4	53.45
3	4	53.35	4	54.15
Margin	12	52.40	12	52.50

Breaker	3		Margin	
	Nobservd	Mean	Nobservd	Mean
Gauger				
1	3	48.87	11	50.89
2	4	45.15	12	49.68
3	4	49.17	12	52.23
Margin	11	47.63	35	50.93

Notice that Genstat has printed the table in two parts, because there is not enough room to fit the whole table across the page.

To examine in detail how the TABULATE statement works, look at the values recorded for the first three samples from the data shown in Section 6.2.1. The value for the first sample (56.0) will be added into the cell of the table indexed by the third level of Gauger and the third level of Breaker — cell i in the schematic table. The value for the second sample (41.8) will be added into the cell indexed by the second level of Gauger and the third level of Breaker — cell f. The value for the third sample (50.2) will be added into cell b, and so on. Every time a value is added into a cell, the count for that cell is increased by one.

The table of numbers of observations has 4 in every non-marginal cell except the cell indexed by the first level of Gauger and the third level of Breaker. One of the values of Strength in this group was missing, and the associated count is therefore 3. For a table that shows the number of missing and non-missing observations for each cell, use the setting 'counts' of the PRINT option:

```
TABULATE [PRINT=counts] STRENGTH
```

As there were four samples for each combination of Gauger and Breaker, the table of 'counts' will have 4 in every non-marginal cell.

The tables above show that the means of the three gaugers differ less than the means of the three breakers. This pattern will be investigated more fully later (Chapter 7, Section 7.2).

6.3 Forming tables classified by more than two factors

Tables can be classified by more than two factors. On two-dimensional paper, the tables have to be displayed in sections showing the summaries classified by only two of the factors; the successive sections display how this two-dimensional table changes for each combination of levels of the remaining factors.

6.3.1 Labelling factor levels

In *Hereditary Genius* (Galton, 1869, Macmillan, London), Francis Galton aimed to show how abilities were inherited. He searched the family trees of illustrious men in various walks of life to discover which of their kinsmen were eminent — not necessarily in the same field. Galton classified the relationships between the illustrious men and their eminent kinsmen as follows:

first degree: father, brother, son;
second degree: grandfather, uncle, nephew, grandson;
third degree: great-grandfather, great-uncle, first cousin, great-nephew, great-grandson.

He also grouped the relationships into those through the male line and those through the female line. Since Galton considered only kinsmen and not kinswomen (who rarely rose to eminence in those male-chauvinist days) all relationships of the first degree are through the male line. Therefore, in order to compare the male and female lines, attention must be confined to the second and third degrees.

The numbers of kinsmen in different categories could be recorded as follows:

Walk of life	Relationship	Line	Number of kinsmen
Law	Grandfather	Male	7
Law	Uncle	Female	9

and so on.

It is the degree of relationship that is of interest, not the actual relationship so the words in the second column can be replaced with the numbers 2 or 3 (2 for both the entries above).

The first three columns can be read into factors. To set up the factor specifying the two degrees of relationship the statement

```
FACTOR [LEVELS=2] Relation
```

might be considered. But this would label the groups of observations 1 and 2 whereas in fact they belong to degrees 2 and 3. To use the latter numbers, a variate must be set up first:

```
VARIATE [VALUES=2,3] Degree; DECIMALS=0
```

The DECIMALS parameter has already been used with a PRINT statement (Chapter 1, Section 1.5). It can also be used when declaring variates and other data structures to control the number of decimal places whenever values of the structure are printed. The setting can be overridden by a setting in a PRINT statement. Here the setting DECIMALS=0 ensures that the values 2 and 3 will be printed as integers. This variate can be connected to the factor Relation by the statement:

```
FACTOR [LEVELS=Degree] Relation
```

The number of values in the variate Degree sets the number of levels of the factor Relation. (The number of values of Relation will be 144, since 144 counts of kinsmen were made.) Moreover, the levels of Relation are labelled by the values of Degree. Thus the first level of Relation is labelled 2 and the second level is labelled 3; and this arrangement is what is wanted here.

The factor and its levels could have been declared in one statement:

```
FACTOR [LEVELS=!V(2,3)] Relation; DECIMALS=0
```

Here the symbol ! indicates that values for an unnamed data structure are to follow in brackets. The symbol V indicates that this structure is a variate; V is the default symbol and it can be omitted (as in Section 3.3.3):

```
FACTOR [LEVELS=!(2,3)] Relation; DECIMALS=0
```

Two other factors are required, one to specify the career followed by the illustrious people whose kinsmen are under study, and the other to specify whether they are related through the male or female line. There were eight careers and two lines, so it might appear that the factors could be set up by the statements:

```
FACTOR [LEVELS=8] Career
&       [LEVELS=2] Line
```

But this will not work because the data for these factors consist of words such as 'Law' and 'Male' rather than numbers. Also it would be clearer if the groups were labelled with the names of the careers instead of the numbers 1 to 8, and the sexes of the lines instead of 1 and 2. Such labels can be specified by declaring text structures as shown below.

```
TEXT [VALUES=Law, Politics, Arms, Letters, Science, Poetry, Art,\
    Church] Carname
& [VALUES=Male,Female] Sex
```

These text structures are connected to the factors Career and Line using the LABELS option, which associates a textual label with each level of a factor. The LEVELS option deals only with the numerical representation of a group.

```
FACTOR [LEVELS=8; LABELS=Carname] Career
&       [LEVELS=2; LABELS=Sex] Line
```

In fact, the number of levels is defined by the number of strings in the text structure, so the LEVELS options need not be set:

```
FACTOR [LABELS=Carname] Career
& [LABELS=Sex] Line
```

Either of these factors could have been declared, together with its labels, in one statement. For example

```
FACTOR [LABELS=!T(Male,Female)] Line
```

As with the levels of the factor Relation the symbol ! indicates that a list of values for an unnamed data structure is to follow. Here they are textual values (strings) so T must be given.

In this example the values of the factors will be read as data but it is possible to declare factor values in the same way as variate values using abbreviated number lists (Chapter 5, Section 5.3.3). Thus if the values of the factor Line were 1 and 2 repeated 72 times the declaration could be

```
FACTOR [LABELS=Sex; VALUES=(1,2)72] Line
```

Note that although the labels are Male and Female the levels 1 and 2 have been used when declaring values. These are the default levels (1 up to the number of levels) as no levels were explicitly declared using the LEVELS option. When printing factor levels, for example to annotate tables, the default levels will be linked with the labels and the names Male and Female will appear on the output. If the levels were explicitly declared as for the factor Relation then these levels would have to be used in the VALUES option. Labels cannot be used in the setting of the VALUES option.

If values for a factor are read, the READ statement also expects to find the numerical levels of a factor by default. However, this can be altered by setting the FREPRESENTATION parameter of the READ statement to 'labels': Genstat will then expect to find the labels in the data, for any factor whose values are being read.

The fourth column of data can be read into a variate called Number.

6.3.2 Forming a three-way table

To show the total number of kinsmen in each category, all three factors must be included in the CLASSIFICATION option of TABULATE:

```
TABULATE [PRINT=total; CLASSIFICATION=Line,Relation,Career] Number
```

When the PRINT option of TABULATE is used, all values in tables are printed with as many decimal places as are needed to give the average value four significant figures. In Galton's time the practice of cutting people into fractions had been abandoned, so it would be preferable to show no decimal places here. This can be done by saving the table using the TOTALS parameter and printing it with a PRINT statement, setting the FIELDWIDTH and DECIMALS parameters to specify that each value shall occupy nine columns and be printed with no decimal places. The complete program and the resulting table are shown below.

```
 1  UNITS[NVALUES=144]
 2  FACTOR[LEVELS=!(2,3)]Relation;DECIMALS=0
 3  TEXT[VALUES=Law,Politics,Arms,Letters,Science,Poetry,Art,\
 4      Church] Carname
 5  &[VALUES=Male,Female]Sex
 6  FACTOR[LABELS=Carname]Career
 7  &[LABELS=Sex]Line
 8  READ Career,Relation,Line,Number;\
 9      FREPRESENTATION=labels,levels,labels,*
```

Identifier	Minimum	Mean	Maximum	Values	Missing	
Number	0.000	1.910	14.000	144	0	Skew

```
58  TABULATE[CLASSIFICATION=Line,Relation,Career]Number;\
59      TOTALS=Kinsmen
60  PRINT Kinsmen;FIELDWIDTH=9;DECIMALS=0
```

Kinsmen

Line	Relation	Career	Law	Politics	Arms	Letters	Science	Poetry
Male	2		41	19	12	18	20	12
	3		16	4	5	7	12	3
Female	2		19	10	6	9	9	1
	3		1	3	2	0	4	0

Line	Relation	Career	Art	Church

Male	2	13	4
	3	4	2
Female	2	3	16
	3	0	0

The identifier Kinsmen now refers to a table structure. Here, the structure is declared automatically by the TABULATE statement, but tables can be declared explicitly, as shown in Section 6.4.1. Whereas variates, texts and factors are one-dimensional structures, tables are multi-dimensional, and so are not printed in the same way by PRINT.

All types of table can be saved by setting parameters of the TABULATE statement, regardless of whether they are also printed by the statement. Thus, the parameter MEANS produces a table of means and NOBSERVATIONS the numbers of observations excluding any whose values are missing. The numbers of missing plus non-missing observations, as produced by the setting 'counts' of the PRINT option, can be saved by the option COUNTS. We have tabulated only one variate at a time, but TABULATE can deal with many variates, saving results in tables for each of the variates. For example, the means of three variates A,B,C classified by factors F and G can be saved as follows, together with the table of counts:

```
TABULATE [CLASSIFICATION=F,G; COUNTS=Tabcnt] A,B,C;
    MEANS=MA,MB,MC
```

An option rather than a parameter is used for saving the 'counts' table because the counts are common to all variates. A parameter is used for the 'nobservations' table because different values may be missing for different variates.

6.3.3 The layout of multiway tables

Note how the table above is laid out. The labels for the factor Career are arranged across the page and the labels for the other two factors down the page. Of these two factors the labels for Relation change more rapidly than those for Line. Remember that the original specification of the table was by the option setting:

```
CLASSIFICATION=Line,Relation,Career
```

Tables classified by as many as nine factors can be handled and the rules for printing them are always the same. The labels of the last factor in the classifying set are printed across the page and the labels of the other factors are printed down the page, those for the penultimate factor changing most rapidly and those for the first factor changing most slowly. By reordering the factor identifiers, the table may fit more neatly on the page. The table was printed without margins because the

MARGINS option was not set to 'yes'.

Storing tables without margins can save a lot of space, especially when they are classified by many factors, and they can be expanded to obtain margins later, as described in the next section.

6.3.4 Margins on multiway tables

The choice of which classifying factor should change most rapidly was an arbitrary one, imposed by the need to present a table classified by three factors on a two-dimensional sheet of paper. You may prefer to think of the table as a box: tables without and with margins could be represented like the one shown in Figure 6.2:

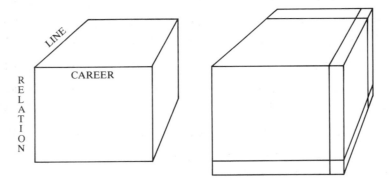

Figure 6.2: Boxes illustrating multiway tables with and without margins

The margins comprise three faces, three edges (themselves margins of the faces) and one corner. It is not possible to make a drawing of a table with four classifying factors or use terms like 'face' and 'edge'. The margins of a four-way table comprise four three-way tables, six two-way tables, four one-way tables and a single cell. This is why margins can take up so much space. If you really want them, however, they can be obtained from the table without margins, Kinsmen, by the statement:

```
MARGIN Kinsmen
```

This expands the table to hold margins and calculates the marginal values. By default, marginal values are formed as totals of the values in the body of the table. Other types of margin can be formed by setting the METHOD parameter; for example:

MARGIN Kinsmen; METHOD=means

The statement

PRINT Kinsmen; FIELDWIDTH=9; DECIMALS=0

produces the output shown below.

Kinsmen

Line	Career Relation	Law	Politics	Arms	Letters	Science	Poetry
Male	2	41	19	12	18	20	12
	3	16	4	5	7	12	3
	Margin	57	23	17	25	32	15
Female	2	19	10	6	9	9	1
	3	1	3	2	0	4	0
	Margin	20	13	8	9	13	1
Margin	2	60	29	18	27	29	13
	3	17	7	7	7	16	3
	Margin	77	36	25	34	45	16

Line	Career Relation	Art	Church	Margin
Male	2	13	4	139
	3	4	2	53
	Margin	17	6	192
Female	2	3	16	73
	3	0	0	10
	Margin	3	16	83
Margin	2	16	20	212
	3	4	2	63
	Margin	20	22	275

This can be regarded as three two-way tables, one below the other. Each two-way table is classified by Career and Relation and has the appropriate margins. The first two-way table refers to Male, the first level of Line, and the second two-way table refers to Female, the second level of Line. The third is a marginal table, totalled over the male and female lines.

6.4 Calculations with tables

6.4.1 Declaring tables

The numbers of kinsmen of illustrious people in some careers were much higher than those of illustrious people in others. So to see if eminent kinsmen are distributed between the two lines and the two degrees in the same way regardless of the career it is helpful to express the counts as percentages of the total count for each career. To do this, a new table is needed to hold the total counts for each career. This could be done by another TABULATE statement:

```
TABULATE [CLASSIFICATION=Career] Number; TOTALS=Cartotal
```

An alternative is to form the new table, Cartotal, directly from the existing table, Kinsmen. This can be done with a CALCULATE statement including the function TTOTAL to total the values in the existing table. But first, the new table must be declared explicitly, so that CALCULATE will produce the totals classified by Career only.

Tables are declared with a TABLE statement. It has options CLASSIFICATION and MARGINS just like the TABULATE statement.

```
TABLE [CLASSIFICATION=Career; MARGINS=yes] Cartotal; DECIMALS=0
```

Several tables can be declared in one statement, if needed, just as for variates and other structures. Similarly, values can be assigned if they are known, using a VALUES option or parameter, and the number of decimal places printed can be set with a DECIMALS parameter.

The total counts can then be extracted from the bottom margin of the table Kinsmen shown above and placed in the one-dimensional table Cartotal using the function TTOTAL:

```
CALCULATE Cartotal = TTOTAL(Kinsmen)
PRINT Cartotal
```

The new table, Cartotal, is as follows:

```
              Cartotal
     Career
        Law        77
   Politics        36
       Arms        25
    Letters        34
    Science        45
     Poetry        16
        Art        20
```

```
Church        22
Margin       275
```

6.4.2 Forming tables of percentages

Another table, Kin%, is now declared to hold the percentages, and the values are formed by a simple CALCULATE statement.

```
TABLE [CLASSIFICATION=Line,Relation,Career; MARGINS=yes] Kin%
CALCULATE Kin% = 100*Kinsmen/Cartotal
```

The CALCULATE statement can operate on values of tables just as it can on values of scalars and variates. Each value of the table Kinsmen is multiplied by 100 and then divided by the relevant value of the table Cartotal — according to the level of the factor Career that classifies both tables — and then stored in the corresponding value of the table Kin%. The table of percentages is printed below.

```
66  TABLE[CLASSIFICATION=Line,Relation,Career;MARGINS=yes]Kin%
67  CALCULATE  Kin%=100*Kinsmen/Cartotal
68  PRINT Kin%
```

		Kin%			
	Career	Law	Politics	Arms	Letters
Line	Relation				
Male	2	53.25	52.78	48.00	52.94
	3	20.78	11.11	20.00	20.59
	Margin	74.03	63.89	68.00	73.53
Female	2	24.68	27.78	24.00	26.47
	3	1.30	8.33	8.00	0.00
	Margin	25.97	36.11	32.00	26.47
Margin	2	77.92	80.56	72.00	79.41
	3	22.08	19.44	28.00	20.59
	Margin	100.00	100.00	100.00	100.00
	Career	Science	Poetry	Art	Church
Line	Relation				
Male	2	44.44	75.00	65.00	18.18
	3	26.67	18.75	20.00	9.09
	Margin	71.11	93.75	85.00	27.27

Female	2	20.00	6.25	15.00	72.73
	3	8.89	0.00	0.00	0.00
	Margin	28.89	6.25	15.00	72.73
Margin	2	64.44	81.25	80.00	90.91
	3	35.56	18.75	20.00	9.09
	Margin	100.00	100.00	100.00	100.00

	Career	Margin
Line	Relation	
Male	2	50.55
	3	19.27
	Margin	69.82
Female	2	26.55
	3	3.64
	Margin	30.18
Margin	2	77.09
	3	22.91
	Margin	100.00

As the totals had already been formed in the margins of the table Kinsmen it is not actually necessary to use the function TTOTAL which forms margins of totals. (A similar function TMEAN forms margins of means.) Here it would have been sufficient to put

```
CALCULATE Cartotal = Kinsmen
```

Note also that the table structure Kin% has exactly the same attributes as Kinsmen. If you had no further use for the values in Kinsmen you could omit the TABLE statement and store the percentages in Kinsmen using the statement

```
CALCULATE Kinsmen = 100*Kinsmen/Cartotal
```

accepting the loss of the old values of Kinsmen.

The percentages of kinsmen in the female line tend to be smaller than those in the male line and Galton suggested that female relatives of illustrious men were fastidious about whom they married. This did not seem to apply to the female relatives of theologians. Poets and artists had a lower percentage of kinsmen in the third degree than some of the other careers and, in fact, Galton found that their kinsmen were mostly in the first degree. He attributed this to the irregular mode of life of poets and artists which militated against their being founders of families.

6.5 Summary

Chapter 6 describes factors and how they can be used to set up tables; also how the tables can be filled with values and then operated on.

Factors have a number of levels (*nlev*) and a number of values (*nval*). They are declared by a FACTOR statement of the form

FACTOR [LEVELS=nlev; NVALUES=nval] factor identifiers

If *nlev* is a number, the levels of the factor will be integers in the range 1 to *nlev*. If *nlev* is a variate, the levels will be the values of the variate.

Factor levels can have labels, which are strings. Such strings can be specified by declaring text structures which are used for setting the LABELS option in the FACTOR statement. They can also be declared directly in the LABELS option.

Factor values can be declared or read. They must be declared as the numbers specified in the LEVELS option, or as the integers 1, 2 ... if the LEVELS option was not set. If read the data must contain the levels unless the FREPRESENTATION parameter of READ is set to 'labels'.

Tables are set up with a TABLE statement of the form:

TABLE [CLASSIFICATION=classifying set; MARGINS=no or yes] Table\
identifiers

The classifying set consists of a list of factors and all tables in the list will have the same classifying set.

Tables will be set up without margins if the MARGINS option is set to 'no', and with margins if it is set to 'yes'. 'No' is the default setting.

Values for tables can be formed using a TABULATE statement of the form

TABULATE [options] list of variates; TOTALS = list of tables;\
  NOBSERVATIONS = list of tables; MEANS = list of tables

The first list specifies the variates to be tabulated and the TOTALS, NOBSER-VATIONS and MEANS lists specify tables to be filled with totals, numbers of observations and means respectively. Any of the last three lists can be omitted.

A table without margins can be expanded to have margins with a MARGIN statement of the form

MARGIN list of tables

Tables in the list must have the same classifying set. Tables can be used as operands in CALCULATE statements just like any other data structure with numeric values, though there are several functions that are appropriate to tables only. If tables occurring in the same CALCULATE statement have different classifying sets special action is taken.

6.6 Exercises

Note: In all these exercises it is assumed that factor values will be declared using abbreviated lists (Sections 5.3.3 and 6.3.1).

6(1) Bond strength was tested on 48 specimens using four different adhesives cured at three different pressures. The adhesives were numbered 1,2,3 and 4 and the pressures were 100psi, 200psi and 300psi. The results are given below.

Adhesive	100psi	200psi	300psi
1	14	14	10
	14	10	12
	14	19	13
	17	15	10
2	11	16	19
	15	15	10
	17	11	14
	30	10	8
3	15	16	18
	23	26	16
	24	25	6
	15	18	22
4	3	20	23
	9	18	12
	6	21	17
	9	10	13

(Example from *Statistics and experimental design in engineering and the physical sciences*, Johnson & Leone, 1967, Wiley, New York.)

Set up a factor for adhesive with levels 1 to 4 and another for pressure with levels 100, 200 and 300. Read the values of bond strength into a variate and form a table (without margins) of mean strength for each combination of adhesive and pressure. Display the table, expand it to have marginal means, and print the expanded table.

6(2) The following meteorological data were collected for two sites in Ayrshire and Cornwall for the first two weeks in February and July during 1977 and 1978.

a)   Rainfall over 24 hours (mm)
b)   Average temperature during the day (°C)
c)   Mean windspeed (m/sec)

			Rainfall	Temperature	Windspeed
Ayrshire	1977	February	5.71	4.49	7.30
			2.20	3.84	7.43
		July	0.50	17.59	4.49
			1.97	16.94	4.63

	1978	February	2.51	4.49	5.14
			0.00	−0.84	2.67
		July	2.99	11.47	7.81
			0.00	13.87	4.57
Cornwall	1977	February	5.66	7.69	4.41
			4.93	7.86	3.00
		July	0.44	17.26	2.37
			5.44	15.76	3.17
	1978	February	3.44	7.47	5.46
			0.29	0.53	4.80
		July	1.70	12.56	5.74
			0.79	14.29	2.86

Each value is a mean over one week. Form three-way tables of means classified by site, year and month for the three variables, and print them side by side with a layout that makes it easy to compare means for different sites in the same month. This can be done most easily by reordering the identifiers of the factors in the CLASSIFICATION option.

6(3) The following petrol consumption figures (in litres per 100 kilometres) were taken from car manufacturers' brochures. M indicates a manual and A an automatic gearbox.

```
M   7.6   M   5.5   M   7.5    M   7.4   M   5.3   M   7.3   M   6.8   M   4.8   M   6.8
M   7.7   M   5.8   M   8.5    A   7.0   A   7.3   A    *    M   7.5   M   5.9   M   8.6
A   7.6   A   7.8   A    *
M   8.9   M   6.3   M   8.3    A   8.1   A   6.9   A   9.2   M   8.6   M   5.5   M   7.5
M   8.9   M   6.1   M   8.4    A   9.0   A   6.9   A   9.4   M   9.5   M   6.5   M   9.4
A   9.7   A   7.2   A  10.6    M   9.5   M   6.4   M   9.0   A   9.8   A   6.9   A   9.8
M   9.8   M   6.0   M   8.3
```

Each triplet of values gives the petrol consumption figures for one car in simulated urban driving and at constant speeds of 90 and of 120 kilometres per hour in that order. The first seven triplets are for cars of 1.0 litre and the last ten for cars of 1.3 litres engine capacity.

Print tables with margins to show total and mean fuel consumptions for cars of different engine capacities being driven at different speeds; also a table of counts of the number of cars in each category.

Form another table with margins classified by engine capacity, driving speed and type of gearbox to show mean fuel consumptions. Print the values of this table with one decimal place. Then express the means as percentages of the mean fuel consumption for cars driven at the three different speeds and print this table.

7 Analysis of designed experiments

7.1 Introduction

An experiment was described earlier (Chapter 6, Section 6.2.1) that aimed to show how measurements of the compressive strength of cement were affected by the person mixing it, the gauger, and the person testing it, the breaker. A table of means was obtained which is shown again below.

Breaker	1	2	3	Mean
Gauger				
1	53.40	49.90	48.87	50.89
2	50.45	53.45	45.15	49.68
3	53.35	54.15	49.17	52.23
Mean	52.40	52.50	47.63	50.93

This table allows you to make a rough, subjective assessment of the importance of the effects of gauger and breaker. For a more detailed and precise assessment an *analysis of variance* is needed.

7.2 Analysis of a completely randomized experiment

7.2.1 Describing the model

In discussing regression analysis the concept of a model was considered (Chapter 4, Section 4.2.1). The model used was

$$\text{pressure}_i = a + b \times \text{age}_i + e_i$$

and the aim was to obtain the estimates of a and b that gave a line of best fit. The concept of a model can be extended to the analysis of factorial experiments. In the cement experiment the model can be written as

$$\text{strength}_{ijk} = \text{mean} + \text{gauger}_j + \text{breaker}_k + \text{gauger . breaker}_{jk} + e_{ijk}$$

where

strength$_{ijk}$	= the strength of the ith sample from the jth gauger and the kth breaker,
mean	= the mean of all the strengths,
gauger$_j$	= the effect of the jth gauger,
breaker$_k$	= the effect of the kth breaker,
gauger.breaker$_{jk}$	= the effect of the interaction of the jth gauger with the kth breaker, and
e_{ijk}	= the residual or error term of the ijkth sample (what is left after the effects of gauger and breaker and their interaction have been removed).

If the effects of the gaugers are consistent for all breakers then the effects of the breakers are equally consistent for all gaugers, and the interaction effects are small. If the effects of the gaugers vary considerably from one breaker to another then the interaction is large. Note that, in Genstat, an interaction is denoted by dot (.) but this symbol can have other meanings in other contexts (see Section 7.3.4). The effects gauger$_j$, breaker$_k$ and gauger.breaker$_{jk}$ are called *treatment effects* in Genstat. They can be specified by a TREATMENTS statement, using the factors that define the groups of samples associated with particular gaugers and breakers (Chapter 6, Section 6.2.1).

```
TREATMENTS Gauger + Breaker + Gauger.Breaker
```

This expression is the part of the model formula that specifies the treatment effects. It can be abbreviated to

```
TREATMENTS Gauger * Breaker
```

The asterisk (*) here indicates 'all combinations of'. Thus the model A*B*C is synonymous with A+B+C+A.B+B.C+A.C+A.B.C.

The mean is subtracted at the start of the analysis since it is the deviations of values of strength from the mean that are analysed. So when the terms in the TREATMENTS statement have been accounted for, all that is left is the term e_{ijk}. This represents the random fluctuations between samples of cement. The variation due to this source will be assigned to a residual or error term automatically and there is no need to mention it explicitly in the Genstat program.

7.2.2 Analysis of variance

Now all that remains is to ask for the analysis of variance of the variate Strength and this is done by the statement:

ANOVA Strength

When tables were produced from the variate Strength a missing value was introduced to illustrate how Genstat would deal with it. To simplify the analysis the recorded number (46.0) will be inserted — for the moment.

The full program and results are shown below.

```
1  UNITS[NVALUES=36]Sample
2  FACTOR[LEVELS=3]Gauger,Breaker
3  READ Sample,Gauger,Breaker,Strength
```

Identifier	Minimum	Mean	Maximum	Values	Missing
Sample	1.00	18.50	36.00	36	0
Strength	41.60	50.80	62.00	36	0

```
12  TREATMENTS Gauger * Breaker
13  ANOVA Strength
```

13 ....

***** Analysis of variance *****

Variate: Strength

Source of variation	d.f.	s.s.	m.s.	v.r.
Gauger	2	40.53	20.27	0.62
Breaker	2	196.74	98.37	3.02
Gauger.Breaker	4	58.83	14.71	0.45
Residual	27	878.91	32.55	
Total	35	1175.01		

***** Tables of means *****

Variate: Strength

Grand mean 50.80

Gauger	1	2	3
	50.48	49.68	52.22

Breaker	1	2	3
	52.40	52.50	47.49

Gauger Breaker	1	2	3
1	53.40	49.90	48.15
2	50.45	53.45	45.15
3	53.35	54.15	49.17

*** Standard errors of differences of means ***

Table	Gauger	Breaker	Gauger Breaker
rep.	12	12	4
s.e.d.	2.329	2.329	4.034

The first section of output produced by the ANOVA statement is the analysis-of-variance table. This is headed by the identifier of the variate analysed, Strength. The table has five columns which will be looked at one by one.

The first column lists the sources of variation. The sources specified by the TREATMENTS statement are all there — the main effects of Gauger and Breaker and their interaction. The Residual term contains what is left after the treatment effects have been removed and is a measure of the variability of samples from the same gauger and breaker.

The second column contains the degrees of freedom (d.f.) for each entry in the first column. For example, two independent comparisons can be made among three gaugers, so the number of degrees of freedom is 2. Similarly, 35 independent comparisons can be made among 36 samples, so the total degrees of freedom are 35. The rationale behind the degrees of freedom for the Gauger.Breaker interaction is a bit more complicated. If you are unfamiliar with this, you should consider reading an introductory textbook such as *Statistics for biologists* (Campbell, 1974, Cambridge University Press).

The next column contains the sums of squares of deviations from the mean, known as the sum of squares (s.s.) for short. Once again, we shall concentrate on Genstat and not go into the way in which the sum of squares is calculated for each term. But note that the sums of squares for the treatment and residual terms add up to the total sum of squares of the deviations of all the values of Strength from the mean.

Inferences made from the analysis are only justified if certain assumptions are valid (see Section 7.4). If they are valid you can proceed with the tests described below.

The fourth column contains mean squares (m.s.), obtained by dividing the corresponding sum of squares by the corresponding degrees of freedom.

The fifth column contains variance ratios (v.r.), often known as *F*-values, obtained by dividing the mean square for the term in question by the residual mean square. If a term has larger effects than would be expected by chance, given the amount of random variation in the experiment, then the variance ratio for that term is substantially larger than 1. Probabilities for the variance ratios can be printed, as a sixth column of the table, by setting the FPROBABILITY option to 'yes'. The default setting is 'no', so no probabilities were printed for this example. The variance ratios in this case indicate that breakers had an appreciable effect on the measurement of compressive strength, but that gaugers did not, and that there was little interaction between breakers and gaugers.

The grand mean comes next, followed by tables of means. Here, the marginal one-way tables for Gauger and Breaker are printed separately from the two-way table for the interaction, but most of the means are the same as those in the table of means produced by TABULATE (Chapter 6, Section 6.2.3). The means for the first gauger, the third breaker, and the combination of these two, are altered by the replacement of the missing value.

The table of standard errors of differences of means enables you to compare means, to see if the differences between them can wholly be accounted for by random fluctuations in the measurements taken. To do this precisely, conditional on the assumptions described in Section 7.4, calculate the t-statistic using the following formula:

$$t = (\text{mean}_1 - \text{mean}_2) \,/\, \text{standard error of difference}$$

and look up its significance in a table such as Table *III* of *Statistical tables* (Fisher & Yates, 1963, Longman, London). The number of degrees of freedom (here 27) are those for the residual term in the analysis of variance table. The table of standard errors has two rows. The first, labelled rep., shows how many units or replicates each mean is based on. Thus, as each gauger mixed 12 samples, the mean for each level of Gauger is the mean of the values for 12 samples. Each combination of gauger and breaker dealt with four samples, so the means for particular Gauger.Breaker combinations are means of four values. The second row gives the standard errors of the differences.

7.2.3 The treatment of missing values

If there is a missing value in the data — the same missing value as before (Chapter 6, Section 6.2.1) — the output is modified as shown below.

```
***** Analysis of variance *****

Variate: Strength
```

Source of variation	d.f.(m.v.)	s.s.	m.s.	v.r.
Gauger	2	39.19	19.60	0.58
Breaker	2	178.25	89.12	2.66
Gauger.Breaker	4	65.31	16.33	0.49
Residual	26(1)	872.74	33.57	
Total	34(1)	1151.34		

```
***** Tables of means *****
```

Variate: Strength

Grand mean 50.88

Gauger	1	2	3
	50.72	49.68	52.22

Breaker	1	2	3
	52.40	52.50	47.73

Gauger	Breaker	1	2	3
1		53.40	49.90	48.87
2		50.45	53.45	45.15
3		53.35	54.15	49.17

*** Standard errors of differences of means ***

Table	Gauger	Breaker	Gauger Breaker
rep.	12	12	4
s.e.d.	2.365	2.365	4.097

(Not adjusted for missing values)

***** Missing values *****

Variate: Strength

Unit	estimate
14	48.87

Max. no. iterations 2

The first modification is in the d.f. column of the analysis of variance table which has an auxiliary missing values (m.v.) column. The missing value reduces the total and residual degrees of freedom by one but since no combination of gauger and breaker has been completely eliminated the number of degrees of freedom for the treatment terms are unchanged.

The numbers in later columns are also modified. The ratios in the v.r. column are different but only slightly so. The tables of means still do not contain identical values to those produced by the TABULATE statement (Chapter 6, Section 6.2.3) even though they are now based on identical data. In the TABULATE table the mean for Gauger 1 was calculated as

$$(4 \times 53.4 + 4 \times 49.9 + 3 \times 48.87)/11 = 50.89$$

In the table of means produced by ANOVA this mean is calculated as

$(4{\times}53.4 + 4{\times}49.9 + 4{\times}48.87)/12 = 50.72$

Genstat estimates a value to substitute for the missing value. The estimate is obtained by an iterative method and 'Max. no. of iterations' refers to the number of cycles of calculation that were required before the method converged to a suitable estimate. A suitable estimate is one that reduces the residual for the missing observation to zero. For example, if the value for the ijkth sample is missing the aim is to reduce the term e_{ijk} of the model formula (Section 7.2.1) to zero — or nearly so. The number of the unit for which the value was missing (14) and the estimated value (48.87) are now given. The fourteenth unit was associated with the first gauger and the third breaker; therefore, in this completely randomized experiment, the estimate for the missing value is the mean for the other three samples dealt with by the first gauger and the third breaker. The general mean has been tried first as a suitable estimate of the missing value: hence the two iterations.

Other information about the analysis can also be displayed if required. The ANOVA statement, like many others, has a PRINT option which controls the output: for example, the setting PRINT=missing gives the section of information about missing values, shown above by default. The setting PRINT=information will give information about the balance of the data. However, rather than analyse the data again just to get this information, an ADISPLAY statement can be given. This shows further results from the latest ANOVA in the same way as an RDISPLAY statement shows results from a FIT statement (Chapter 4, Section 4.4.5).

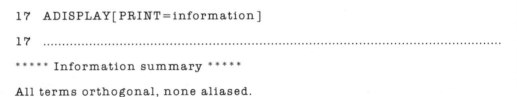

```
17  ADISPLAY[PRINT=information]

17  ..............................................................................................................

***** Information summary *****

All terms orthogonal, none aliased.
```

The information summary states that all the treatment terms are *orthogonal* and none are *aliased*. This is a precise, technical way of stating that the design of the experiment was balanced, which greatly simplifies the interpretation of the analysis. If you need a fuller explanation of these terms, see a book such as *Statistical methods* (Snedecor & Cochran, 1980, Iowa State Press, Ames).

7.3 A split-plot design

Genstat has a powerful procedure for the analysis of more complex experimental designs and an example follows. But a knowledge of this rather specialized subject is not necessary for an understanding of the rest of the book and you can skip this section if it is not relevant to your needs.

7.3.1 The layout of the experiment

The next example is drawn from *The design and analysis of factorial experiments* (Yates, 1964, Commonwealth Agricultural Bureau, Farnham Royal). It concerns an experiment on three varieties of oats grown with four rates of nitrogenous fertilizer.

Each of the three varieties was grown on a plot of land which was divided into four sub-plots, and a different rate of nitrogen was applied to each sub-plot. This gave 12 treatment combinations (three varieties × four rates of nitrogen). As it was expected that yield would differ from one part of the field to another, the 12 treatment combinations were replicated six times (giving 18 plots and 72 sub-plots) and each replicate occupied a particular part of the field. The replicates, each comprising a complete set of 12 treatments, were called blocks and the experimental layouts for the first and last blocks are shown below.

	Variety	Rate of nitrogen (cwt/acre)	
Block 1	Marvellous	0.6	0.4
		0.2	0.0
	Victory	0.0	0.2
		0.6	0.4
	Golden Rain	0.0	0.2
		0.4	0.6
	.	.	.
	.	.	.
	.	.	.
Block 6	Victory	0.4	0.0
		0.6	0.2
	Golden Rain	0.6	0.4
		0.0	0.2
	Marvellous	0.0	0.2
		0.4	0.6

In this experiment the sources of variation in yield are of two types. Firstly, there are those sources in which the experimenter is primarily interested — the effects of variety and nitrogen. As mentioned earlier these are called the treatment effects in Genstat. Secondly, there are those sources of variation that tend to mask the treatment effects — in this experiment, position in the field where some areas may be more favourable to growth than others. In Genstat such sources are called *block effects*. The experimenter usually wishes to do two things with variation from sources of the second type:

a)   . to eliminate, as far as possible, its influence on the estimation of treatment effects and

b)   to use it as a measure of random fluctuations against which to test the treatment effects.

This is not the place for a full introduction to the way in which analysis of variance achieves these aims, but the subject is covered in many texts; for example, *Experimental designs* (Cochran & Cox, 1957, Wiley, New York) gives a full account of many experimental designs, most of which can be analysed with Genstat.

A table showing the arrangement of blocks, plots and sub-plots separately from that of varieties and rates of nitrogen is given below. It will be used to distinguish the different types of effects defined by model formulae in Genstat and will help to illustrate how the values for the factors used in the formulae are declared or read.

Block	Plot	Sub-plot				Variety	Rate of Nitrogen (cwt/acre)			
1	1	1	2	3	4	Marvellous	0.6	0.4	0.2	0.0
	2	1	2	3	4	Victory	0.0	0.2	0.6	0.4
	3	1	2	3	4	Golden Rain	0.0	0.2	0.4	0.6
2	1	1	2	3	4	Marvellous	0.4	0.0	0.2	0.6
	2	1	2	3	4	Victory	0.6	0.0	0.2	0.4
	3	1	2	3	4	Golden Rain	0.2	0.0	0.4	0.6
3	1	1	2	3	4	Golden Rain	0.2	0.4	0.6	0.0
	2	1	2	3	4	Marvellous	0.6	0.2	0.4	0.0
	3	1	2	3	4	Victory	0.0	0.6	0.2	0.4
4	1	1	2	3	4	Marvellous	0.4	0.6	0.0	0.2
	2	1	2	3	4	Golden Rain	0.0	0.4	0.6	0.2
	3	1	2	3	4	Victory	0.2	0.4	0.6	0.0
5	1	1	2	3	4	Golden Rain	0.6	0.0	0.4	0.2
	2	1	2	3	4	Victory	0.4	0.6	0.0	0.2
	3	1	2	3	4	Marvellous	0.4	0.6	0.2	0.0
6	1	1	2	3	4	Victory	0.4	0.0	0.6	0.2
	2	1	2	3	4	Golden Rain	0.6	0.4	0.0	0.2
	3	1	2	3	4	Marvellous	0.0	0.2	0.4	0.6

On the left is shown how the blocks were divided into plots which were further subdivided into sub-plots. These groupings, indicating position in the field, can be used to define the block effects. As before, factors will be used to specify groupings and the factors defining block effects will be called *block factors*. The oat varieties grown on each plot and the rates of nitrogen applied to each sub-plot are shown on the right of the table. These groupings define the treatment effects and the factors used to specify them will be called *treatment factors*. Note how the groupings for block and treatment effects run in parallel to each other.

In order to analyse this experiment, you need to specify the block and the plot within that block and the sub-plot within that plot to which each experimental unit belongs (the block factors). You also need to specify the variety that was grown on each experimental unit and the level of nitrogen that was applied to it (the treatment factors).

7.3.2 Block effects

As shown in the table in Section 7.3.1 the blocks were numbered 1 to 6, the plots within each block 1 to 3 and the sub-plots within each plot 1 to 4. Assuming that the standard number of values (here 72) for variates and factors has already been declared with a UNITS statement, the block factors can be declared with the following statements:

```
FACTOR [LEVELS=6] Block & [LEVELS=3] Plot & [LEVELS=4] Subplot
```

The values of the block factors could be read in along with the values of the treatment factors and the yields, but since they follow regular patterns the effort of typing them in with the data can be avoided. Chapter 6, Section 6.3.1 showed how values can be assigned to factors. If the data are read in the order shown in the table in Section 7.3.1 the values of Block consist of 12 ones followed by 12 twos and so on up to 12 sixes. Pre-multiplication repeats each element in a number list (Chapter 5, Section 5.3.3) so this sequence of values can be represented by 12(1...6). These values are put into the factor statement thus:

```
FACTOR [LEVELS=6; VALUES=12(1...6)] Block
```

Next consider the factor Plot. In each block the first four sub-plots belong to Plot 1, the next four to Plot 2 and the last four to Plot 3. This can be represented by 4(1...3). But this sequence is needed six times, once for each block; this can be done by post-multiplication, thus: 4(1...3)6. The values of the factor Subplot are simply the sequence 1 to 4, repeated 18 times, thus: (1...4)18. These values can be put into the FACTOR statements as follows:

```
FACTOR [LEVELS=6; VALUES=12(1...6)] Block
&         [LEVELS=3; VALUES=4(1...3)6] Plot
&         [LEVELS=4; VALUES=(1...4)18] Subplot
```

7.3.3 Treatment effects

Factors to specify the treatment effects are now required. As described earlier (Chapter 6, Section 6.3.1), factors can be specified with textual labels to be used when printing results classified by the factors. For the factor Variety, the variety names can be used:

```
FACTOR [LABELS=!T(Victory,'Golden Rain',Marvellous)] Variety
```

Note that the string Golden Rain, which includes a space, has to be enclosed in single quotes.

For nitrogen, it would be appropriate to print real numbers representing the rates of application in cwt/acre. This can be done by specifying the rates as the levels of the factor:

```
FACTOR [LEVELS=!(0.0,0.2,0.4,0.6)] Nitrogen
```

The values of the treatment factors and the variate Yield are now read in and a PRINT statement is added to check that everything is right. The values for Variety were recorded as 1, 2, or 3 rather than Victory, 'Golden Rain', or Marvellous, so there is no need to set the FREPRESENTATION parameter of the READ statement as in Chapter 6 (Section 6.3.1).

The program so far, and its output, are shown below. Note how the values for the block and treatment factors are in the same order as those shown in the table in Section 7.3.1.

```
1   UNITS[NVALUES=72]
2   FACTOR[LEVELS=6;VALUES=12(1...6)]Block
3   &      [LEVELS=3;VALUES=4(1...3)6]Plot
4   &      [LEVELS=4;VALUES=(1...4)18]Subplot
5   FACTOR[LABELS=!T(Victory,'GoldenRain',Marvellous)]Variety
6   FACTOR[LEVELS=!(0.0,0.2,0.4,0.6)]Nitrogen
7   READ Variety,Nitrogen,Yield
```

Identifier	Minimum	Mean	Maximum	Values	Missing
Yield	9.46	18.57	31.07	72	0

```
23   PRINT Block,Plot,Subplot,Variety,Nitrogen,Yield
```

Block	Plot	Subplot	Variety	Nitrogen	Yield
1	1	1	Marvellous	0.6000	27.86
1	1	2	Marvellous	0.4000	21.07
1	1	3	Marvellous	0.2000	25.00
1	1	4	Marvellous	0.0000	18.75
1	2	1	Victory	0.0000	19.82
1	2	2	Victory	0.2000	23.21
1	2	3	Victory	0.6000	31.07
1	2	4	Victory	0.4000	28.04
1	3	1	Golden Rain	0.0000	20.89
1	3	2	Golden Rain	0.2000	20.36
1	3	3	Golden Rain	0.4000	28.75

1	3	4	Golden Rain	0.6000	25.18
2	1	1	Marvellous	0.4000	18.57
2	1	2	Marvellous	0.0000	12.50
2	1	3	Marvellous	0.2000	15.89
2	1	4	Marvellous	0.6000	20.89
2	2	1	Victory	0.6000	21.79
2	2	2	Victory	0.0000	13.21
2	2	3	Victory	0.2000	15.89
2	2	4	Victory	0.4000	14.46
2	3	1	Golden Rain	0.2000	18.39
2	3	2	Golden Rain	0.0000	11.43
2	3	3	Golden Rain	0.4000	23.57
2	3	4	Golden Rain	0.6000	23.75
3	1	1	Golden Rain	0.2000	19.29
3	1	2	Golden Rain	0.4000	22.50
3	1	3	Golden Rain	0.6000	26.61
3	1	4	Golden Rain	0.0000	12.50
3	2	1	Marvellous	0.6000	25.71
3	2	2	Marvellous	0.2000	22.14
3	2	3	Marvellous	0.4000	21.61
3	2	4	Marvellous	0.0000	17.14
3	3	1	Victory	0.0000	10.89
3	3	2	Victory	0.6000	17.86
3	3	3	Victory	0.2000	16.25
3	3	4	Victory	0.4000	17.32
4	1	1	Marvellous	0.4000	19.46
4	1	2	Marvellous	0.6000	17.68
4	1	3	Marvellous	0.0000	11.25
4	1	4	Marvellous	0.2000	12.50
4	2	1	Golden Rain	0.0000	14.29
4	2	2	Golden Rain	0.4000	16.79
4	2	3	Golden Rain	0.6000	22.50
4	2	4	Golden Rain	0.2000	14.64
4	3	1	Victory	0.2000	16.07
4	3	2	Victory	0.4000	17.86
4	3	3	Victory	0.6000	20.71
4	3	4	Victory	0.0000	11.07
5	1	1	Golden Rain	0.6000	17.14
5	1	2	Golden Rain	0.0000	10.71
5	1	3	Golden Rain	0.4000	15.89

5	1	4	Golden Rain	0.2000	18.21
5	2	1	Victory	0.4000	20.00
5	2	2	Victory	0.6000	15.36
5	2	3	Victory	0.0000	12.14
5	2	4	Victory	0.2000	11.43
5	3	1	Marvellous	0.4000	23.57
5	3	2	Marvellous	0.6000	22.14
5	3	3	Marvellous	0.2000	23.04
5	3	4	Marvellous	0.0000	15.89
6	1	1	Victory	0.4000	21.07
6	1	2	Victory	0.0000	9.46
6	1	3	Victory	0.6000	20.18
6	1	4	Victory	0.2000	13.21
6	2	1	Golden Rain	0.6000	18.57
6	2	2	Golden Rain	0.4000	15.36
6	2	3	Golden Rain	0.0000	15.89
6	2	4	Golden Rain	0.2000	14.64
6	3	1	Marvellous	0.0000	17.32
6	3	2	Marvellous	0.2000	17.68
6	3	3	Marvellous	0.4000	21.25
6	3	4	Marvellous	0.6000	21.61

7.3.4 Specifying error models

The model that is used to analyse this experiment can be expressed as

$$\text{yield}_{ijklm} = \text{mean} + \text{block}_i + \text{block}\,.\,\text{plot}_{ij} + \text{block}\,.\,\text{plot}\,.\,\text{subplot}_{ijk}$$
$$+ \text{variety}_l + \text{nitrogen}_m + \text{variety}\,.\,\text{nitrogen}_{lm}$$

Each plot is identified by terms involving blocks, plots and sub-plots only. But the yield for each plot is affected also by the variety grown and the rate of nitrogen applied. This distinction between the terms specifying the experimental layout and the terms specifying the treatments applied was illustrated in the table in Section 7.3.1.

The terms on the second line of the formula define the treatment effects. Here the term variety.nitrogen$_{lm}$ follows after the corresponding main effect terms variety$_l$ and nitrogen$_m$. It therefore denotes the interaction between nitrogen and variety by the same convention as in the previous example (Section 7.2.1).

The terms on the first line of the formula define the block effects. However, block.plot$_{ij}$ follows after block$_i$ but not after plot$_j$. The latter term is not mentioned at all. Unlike the lth variety, which is always the same variety no matter how much nitrogen you put on it, the jth plot in Block 1 does not correspond in any way to the *j*th plot in Block 2. It would therefore be inappropriate to refer to a main effect of plot and the model term block.plot$_{ij}$ denotes not the interaction between the *i*th block and the *j*th plot but the effect of the *j*th plot *within* the *i*th block. Similarly, the term block.plot.subplot$_{ijk}$ denotes the effect of the *k*th sub-plot within the *j*th plot within the *i*th block.

The experimenter did not lay out his experiment in blocks, plots and sub-plots because he was primarily interested in them. He hoped to get better estimates of the treatment effects (variety, nitrogen and their interaction) by abstracting the variation due to blocks, plots and sub-plots or using it to obtain residual terms against which the treatment effects can be tested. A practical consideration was that it is easier to spread fertilizer than sow seed on the relatively small sub-plots. In the previous example (Section 7.2.1) you only needed to specify the treatment terms of the model in the Genstat program: the presence of the residual term in the single error stratum was implicit. In the present case, the presence of block effects makes the error structure of the experiment more complex and you must describe it before asking for the analysis of variance. This can be done by means of a BLOCKS statement, using the factors just declared:

```
BLOCKS Block+Block.Plot+Block.Plot.Subplot
```

This can be abbreviated to

```
BLOCKS Block/Plot/Subplot
```

where the slash (/) denotes 'within', as in 'Plot within Block'.

The BLOCKS statement can be regarded as specifying

a)   the layout of the experiment,
b)   the block effects that the layout accounts for, and
c)   the number of error terms since blocks, plots and sub-plots will each be associated with a separate error.

Most computer programs for the analysis of experiments provide for only one error term, as for the regression statements in Genstat (Chapter 5).

7.3.5 The split-plot analysis

The treatment effects are specified as before.

```
TREATMENTS Variety*Nitrogen
```

This indicates that terms for variety, nitrogen and their interaction are to be included in the model.

An analysis of variance of the variate Yield is asked for by putting

ANOVA [PRINT=aovtable] Yield

The rest of the program and its results are as shown below.

```
24   BLOCKS Block / Plot / Subplot
25   TREATMENTS Variety * Nitrogen
26   ANOVA [PRINT=aovtable] Yield
```

26   ....

***** Analysis of variance *****

Variate: Yield

Source of variation	d.f.	s.s.	m.s.	v.r.
Block stratum	5	506.340	101.268	
Block.Plot stratum				
Variety	2	56.981	28.490	1.49
Residual	10	191.799	19.180	
Block.Plot.Subplot stratum				
Nitrogen	3	638.700	212.900	37.71
Variety.Nitrogen	6	10.290	1.715	0.30
Residual	45	254.036	5.645	
Total	71	1658.147		

The analysis of variance table has been divided into three strata, each with its own residual term. As specified by the BLOCKS statement, these strata are labelled Block, Block.Plot and Block.Plot.Subplot. No treatment was applied to complete blocks, so there is only one line for the Block stratum. This is for a residual term, a summary of the variation between blocks.

In this experiment the three treatment terms are not all in the same stratum. Genstat automatically determines which treatment terms to assign to each stratum from the values of the factors used in the BLOCKS and TREATMENTS statements. For example the values for the first and second plots in the first block are

Block	Plot	Subplot	Variety	Nitrogen
1	1	1	Marvellous	0.6
1	1	2	Marvellous	0.4

1	1	3	Marvellous	0.2
1	1	4	Marvellous	0.0
1	2	1	Victory	0.0
1	2	2	Victory	0.2
1	2	3	Victory	0.6
1	2	4	Victory	0.4

From these factor values it can be worked out that the variety Marvellous is grown on the whole of Plot 1 and the variety Victory on the whole of Plot 2; but that each rate of nitrogen was applied to one sub-plot in each of the plots.

Since a given variety was grown over a whole plot, estimates of varietal effects are shown in the plots-within-blocks stratum. The plots are like experimental units as far as the variety effects are concerned; the sub-plots within them cannot make independent contributions to the estimate of error variance since they not only bear the same variety but are also grouped together in space. The Variety mean square is therefore divided by the 'Residual' mean square in the Block.Plot stratum (19.180) and the resulting small variance ratio indicates that the varietal effects are negligible. However, different levels of nitrogen have been applied to each sub-plot so the effect of nitrogen and of the interaction of nitrogen with variety are estimated in the Block.Plot.Subplot stratum and their variance ratios are calculated by dividing their mean squares by the residual mean square in that stratum (5.645).

The variance ratio for nitrogen indicates that the different rates of application had an important effect on yield but the variance ratio for the interaction shows that the effects of different rates of nitrogen were consistent over all varieties.

In this table the 'Total' line contains total degrees of freedom and sums of squares over all three strata.

The tables of means can be printed by an ADISPLAY statement.

```
27  ADISPLAY[PRINT=means]

27  ...........................................................................................
***** Tables of means *****
```

Variate: Yield

Grand mean 18.57

Variety	Victory	Golden Rain	Marvellous
	17.43	18.66	19.61

Nitrogen	0.00	0.20	0.40	0.60
	14.18	17.66	20.40	22.03

Variety Nitrogen	0.00	0.20	0.40	0.60
Victory	12.77	16.01	19.79	21.16
Golden Rain	14.29	17.59	20.48	22.29
Marvellous	15.48	19.38	20.92	22.65

*** Standard errors of differences of means ***

Table	Variety	Nitrogen	Variety Nitrogen
rep.	24	18	6
s.e.d.	1.264	0.792	1.735

Except when comparing means with the same level(s) of Variety   1.372

The tables of means are similar to those in the previous example but the table of standard errors of the differences is not. There are two standard errors for the comparison of Variety.Nitrogen combinations.

When comparing combinations which come from the same row of the table, and hence have the same level of Variety, the appropriate error is calculated from the residual mean square for the Block.Plot.Subplot stratum. It is in fact

$$\sqrt{((2 \times 5.645)/6)} = 1.372$$

But when comparing means from different rows of the table and thus from different varieties two errors are involved; firstly the plot error, used for comparing varietal differences; secondly the sub-plot error, used for comparing differences between rates of application of nitrogen. So this standard error is calculated as a weighted mean of the two error terms. It is

$$\sqrt{(2 \times ((4-1) \times 5.645 + 19.180)/(4 \times 6))} = 1.735$$

The method of calculating this error is given in *Experimental designs*.

7.4 Saving results from an analysis of variance

When drawing conclusions from an analysis of variance several assumptions are made. These are

a)   that the terms in the model are additive (all the terms in the models shown above are connected by + signs),

b)   that the magnitude of the residuals (block effects) remains approximately constant over the full range of the measurements recorded,

c)   that the residuals are Normally distributed.

Some of these assumptions can be roughly checked by drawing graphs of the residuals (values of block.plot.subplot$_{ijk}$). There are many popular forms of display described in several statistics books, such as *Applied regression analysis* (Draper & Smith, 1981, Wiley, New York). But one useful form is a plot of residuals against fitted values; that is, the values of yield$_{ijk}$ - block.plot.subplot$_{ijk}$ (see Chapter 4, Section 4.5).

If the plotted points can be roughly contained within two parallel lines, equally spaced about the line through zero for residuals, then it is likely that the assumptions are justified. This situation is illustrated in Figure 7.1.

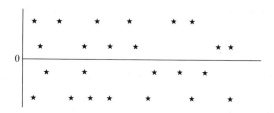

Figure 7.1: Plot of residuals against fitted values: no violation of assumptions underlying analysis of variance

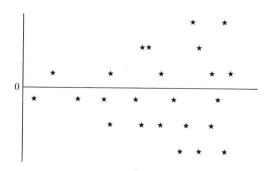

Figure 7.2: Plot of residuals against fitted values: magnitude of errors inconstant

A pattern such as that shown in Figure 7.2 would indicate that the magnitude of the errors is not constant and some transformation of the data or some form of weighted analysis is required.

It is easy to draw these graphs in Genstat. The results from an analysis of variance can be saved in a similar way to the results of a regression analysis (Chapter 4, Section 4.2.3). The residuals and fitted values can be saved as variates by giving a further ADISPLAY statement as follows:

```
ADISPLAY [PRINT=*] RESIDUALS=Resids; FITTEDVALUES=Fitted
```

The PRINT option is set to missing so that no further output is produced. A GRAPH statement is then used to plot one variate against the other.

```
GRAPH Y = Resids; X = Fitted
```

The resulting plot is shown below.

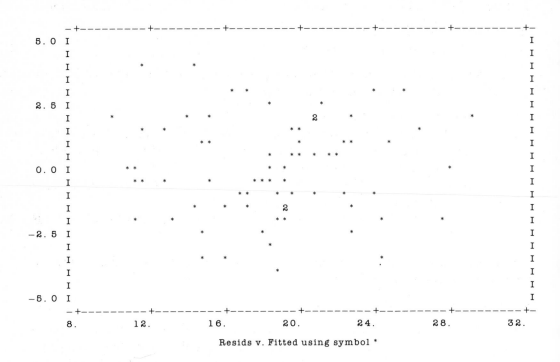

Resids v. Fitted using symbol *

```
28   ADISPLAY[PRINT = *]RESIDUALS = Resids;FITTEDVALUES = Fitted
29   GRAPH[NROWS = 21;NCOLUMNS = 61]Y = Resids;X = Fitted
```

Strictly speaking, this plot only checks the assumptions in the bottom stratum of the analysis, but it is likely that any breaches of the assumptions would show up in this stratum. As the points can be contained within two lines parallel to the line through zero for residuals, the assumptions appear to be valid.

7.5 Summary

The model formula used to express the value for any experimental unit is split up as follows:

value = mean + block effect terms + treatment effect terms

The block effect terms and the treatment effect terms are specified using BLOCKS and TREATMENTS statements of the form:

BLOCKS block effect terms
TREATMENTS treatment effect terms

The block and treatment effect terms are specified using model formulae. In these formulae, if A, B, and C are factor identifiers, then:

A   represents the main effect of A
A.B   represents the interaction of A and B if the main effects of A and B have already been estimated, or the effect of B within A if only the main effect of A has already been estimated.
A*B*C   represents A + B + C + A.B + A.C + B.C + A.B.C; that is, all possible combinations of A, B, and C
A/B   represents A + A.B; that is, the main effect of A and the effect of B within A

Once the block and treatment effect terms have been specified, the analysis of variance is asked for by an ANOVA statement of the form:

ANOVA list of variates

Some assumptions underlying any conclusion drawn from the analysis of variance can be checked by saving the fitted values and residuals and then plotting one against the other. The fitted values and residuals can be saved by using an ADISPLAY statement of the form:

ADISPLAY RESIDUALS = list of variates; FITTEDVALUES = list of variates

The PRINT option of ANOVA and ADISPLAY include the following settings:

aovtable   analysis-of-variance table,
means   tables of means and standard errors of differences,
missing   information about missing values, and
information summary of balance.

7.6 Exercises

7(1) The effects of four diets on the livers of rats were investigated in an experiment. The liver weights, expressed as percentages of the body weight, are presented below.

Diet	1	2	3	4
	3.42	3.17	3.34	3.64
	3.96	3.63	3.72	3.93
	3.87	3.38	3.81	3.77
	4.19	3.47	3.66	4.18
	3.58	3.39	3.55	4.21
	3.76	3.41	3.51	3.88
	3.84	3.55		3.96
		3.44		3.91

(Example from *Statistics for biologists*, Campbell, 1974, Cambridge University Press).

Put these data into a form suitable for reading by Genstat and perform an analysis of variance on them. Remember that the observations from all the four diets must go into a single variate. The diets associated with each liver weight can be presented in parallel and read with the liver weights, or the values for the factor specifying the diet can be declared using an abbreviated number list as described in Chapter 5 (Section 5.3.3). Genstat will take care of the fact that the numbers of weights for each diet are not equal.

7(2) The response of four rabbits to four doses of insulin A, B, C, and D was investigated in a Latin Square design with rabbits as columns and dates of injection as rows. The results are given below.

Rabbit		1		2		3		4
Date in April								
23	B	24	C	46	D	34	A	48
25	D	33	A	58	B	57	C	60
26	A	57	D	26	C	60	B	45
27	C	46	B	34	A	61	D	47

(Example from *Statistics in Biology*, Bliss, 1967, McGraw-Hill, New York).

Write a Genstat program to perform an analysis of variance on these data. Only the doses and responses should be read as data. In a Latin Square design, the effects of both rows and columns are treated as block effects.

7(3) An experiment was conducted to determine the effect of cultivation sequence and weed control method on the yield of sugar beet. The experiment was planned in three randomized blocks and the yield of each plot was measured by two sugar estimation methods. The experiment thus had a split-plot design, with individual sugar estimations being the 'sub-plots'. The results are shown below.

	Weed control system	Sugar estimation method	Cultivation sequence			
			P	Q	R	S
Block I	V	M	4.73	4.65	8.70	10.78
		N	0.61	6.31	3.45	8.49
	W	M	4.36	6.02	9.29	13.13
		N	5.65	9.74	7.63	12.00
Block II	V	M	3.23	6.29	3.69	6.95
		N	1.66	4.41	3.48	5.70
	W	M	2.10	5.92	9.42	10.09
		N	3.54	7.38	7.72	9.62
Block III	V	M	3.69	6.12	6.41	8.91
		N	4.84	0.78	7.03	5.96
	W	M	6.99	8.33	8.52	11.21
		N	4.04	8.64	8.10	7.88

(Example adapted from *Statistics for biologists*, Campbell, 1974, Cambridge University Press).

Write a Genstat program to analyse this experiment.

8   Programming: suiting analysis to your problem

8.1 Introduction

You can use a computer in a variety of ways to analyse data. Sometimes a particular approach is imposed by the constraints of the computer system, but sometimes you can adopt an approach to suit your own preferences. For example, some people like to carry out statistical analyses such as regression interactively: that is, seeing the results of fitting each model before choosing the next. This method was tacitly assumed in Chapter 4 (Section 4.4) for example. But most large-scale analyses of designed experiments are carried out in batch where the whole job is run and the results are inspected at leisure.

When you want to work in batch, or have to because of your computing system, you will often do a series of analyses in one program. It can then be very useful to be able to make the form of one analysis dependent on the results of a previous one in the same program. This chapter shows you several ways to specify this dependence in general calculations and displays.

There are many other ways in which a Genstat program can be tailored to the problems presented by your particular investigation. We shall start by looking at one of the first problems you may encounter after collecting masses of data, when you want to use some of the data for an analysis but not all of it.

8.2 Selecting the data you want

8.2.1 Reading a subset of the variables

An opinion poll was carried out to provide data for research into political attitudes. Each person in a large sample was asked a number of questions about their support for political parties and their feelings about the current Government, and the replies were recorded together with several personal variables such as age and income (if revealed!). This large amount of information is intended for use in a number of separate studies of various aspects of the survey. We shall examine one aspect, namely the connection between support for each political party and the age and income of the supporter.

The data have been stored in the computer in a concise form to save space. The answers from each person interviewed are coded on one line, or *record*, in the data file and every item of information occupies a fixed group of columns, called a *field*, in this line. The results to be investigated are available as follows:

information	columns occupied
age	24–25
income	26–30
party	43

The ages and incomes are recorded in whole numbers, whereas the parties are coded A to H, representing the various national parties and some smaller local ones; the code Z is used for people who said 'Don't know' or did not state any allegiance.

Here is the record of information from one of the people interviewed:

```
0004226 AFS0434 1YN006M4207430 3407100091 B00410411
                              ^         ^           ^
```

The carets (^) show you where the age, income and party are recorded: this person is 42, earns £7430 per year and supports the party coded as B.

There are two problems with reading these data. Firstly, on each record there is extra information that is not wanted, and secondly the data are not in free format; that is, the values are not separated by spaces or any other separator. The READ statement in Genstat has been designed to cope with practically any method of recording data values, including this comparatively simple one. You have seen the simplest form of READ in many examples in the preceding chapters with data values in free format:

```
READ P,Q,R
```

where P, Q, and R are the identifiers of data structures. In the present example the layout has a *fixed format* — data values occupy a fixed group of columns on each record — and the statement must include information specifying which columns are to be read. So, after declarations of variates Age and Income and a factor Party to store the data, the statement to read the values will be:

```
READ [LAYOUT=fixedfield; SKIP=*] Age,Income,Party;
    FIELDWIDTH=2,5,1; SKIP=23,0,12
```

The option LAYOUT is used to indicate that the data are in fixed format; the default is LAYOUT=separated. The option SKIP=* indicates that after the values for each unit have been read (in this case each individual), Genstat is to skip to the beginning of the next line. This is important, since otherwise the next value of Age will be read from the same line. The parameter FIELDWIDTH indicates how many columns each value occupies; thus Age occupies two columns. The parameter SKIP (as distinct from the option SKIP) indicates how many columns are to be skipped before reading a value; thus, starting from the beginning of a line, 23 columns are skipped before reading a value of Age, then no columns are skipped before reading the corresponding value of Income.

8.2.2 Defining the end of data

The data recorded from the survey were intended for many applications, and had to be used by many people working with different computer languages. One result of this was that there was no colon or any other marker at the end of the data file. Without such a marker, Genstat must be told the number of values to look for, and that there is no marker. The following statements read the records from the 1723 people surveyed:

```
VARIATE [NVALUES=1723] Age, Income
FACTOR [NVALUES=1723; LABELS=!T(A,B,C,D,E,F,G,H,Z)] Party
READ [CHANNEL=2; LAYOUT=fixedfield; SKIP=*; END=*]\
    Age,Income,Party; FIELDWIDTH=2,5,1; SKIP=23,0,12;\
    FREPRESENTATION=labels
```

The option setting END=* indicates that there is no end-of-data marker. The asterisk (*) normally stands for a missing value in data or for an unset value of an option or parameter, so this option setting can be interpreted as meaning 'No end-of-data marker is set'. By contrast, the setting END='*' would mean that the asterisk character was the end-of-data marker. Any string can be specified as the terminator; for example, END='END OF DATA'. The setting END=* has potential dangers because if the sample were miscounted you might miss out the answers from the last few people in the survey. However, you may want to miss out some of the answers: this setting can be used to read just the first 1000 records, say. If you want to select from the records in any other way, though, the method in Section 8.2.3 must be used.

If the number in the sample is not known, there is no alternative to putting a terminator at the end of the data. But having done this, it is not necessary to count up the number in order to declare the length of the structure. Provided that a terminator is present, the length of the structures can be defined from the number of values actually found when reading, by setting another option called SETNVALUES:

```
FACTOR [LABELS=!T(A,B,C,D,E,F,G,H,Z)] Party
OPEN 'SURVEY.DAT'; CHANNEL=2
READ [CHANNEL=2; LAYOUT=fixedfield; SKIP=*; SETNVALUES=yes]
    Age,Income,Party; FIELDWIDTH=2,5,1; SKIP=23,0,12;
    FREPRESENTATION=labels
```

Such a program may be reused with other data sets which may have different numbers of values. Again there are dangers, because some of the data may have been incorrectly recorded, so it is best if the number can be checked.

8.2.3 Analysing a subset of the observations

Having read the data, the required summaries of the survey can be produced. First we shall draw some histograms, using the HISTOGRAM statement introduced in Chapter 3 (Section 3.2), to show the age distribution of people supporting the three most popular parties in this survey: these are the ones coded A, B and C. The ages of the supporters of the first party are those values in the variate Age corresponding to the values coded A in the factor Party. To produce the histogram of just these ages, excluding the others, the RESTRICT statement is used to restrict attention temporarily to this subset of the data:

```
RESTRICT Age; Party .EQ. 1
```

The item .EQ. is an *operator* that compares numbers in data structures on either side of it. Here, it compares the values of Party with the number 1. The result is recorded as 1 if the values are equal, or 0 if not; RESTRICT then confines the operation of subsequent statements that operate with Age to those units for which the value is 1. Logical operators like .EQ. can be thought of as having the results 'true' and 'false', but Genstat does not have special data structures for storing such logical values and the numbers 1 and 0 are used instead. In the RESTRICT statement, as in all Genstat statements, you must refer to factor levels by the values defined as their levels when declared, or the ordinals 1, 2, and so on if the LEVELS option was not set (thus, the label A should not be used in the RESTRICT statement).

There are other operators like .EQ. that compare numbers. They can be used in any statement that allows an expression, such as a CALCULATE statement, for example. If preferred, there are shorter forms for these operators made up from the symbols $< > /$ and $=$.

.GT. or $>$	Greater Than,
.LT. or $<$	Less Than,
.LE. or $<=$	Less than or Equal to,
.GE. or $>=$	Greater than or Equal to,

.EQ. or ==   EQual to, and
.NE. or /= or <>   Not Equal to.

Subsequent statements that use the variate Age will now confine attention to the values we want until a new RESTRICT statement is given. (A few statements, such as READ, ignore restrictions.) Thus

```
HISTOGRAM Age
```

prints the histogram for the first party, and it is easy, though a bit repetitive, to obtain the other two histograms in the same way:

```
RESTRICT Age; Party .EQ. 2
HISTOGRAM Age
RESTRICT Age; Party .EQ. 3
HISTOGRAM Age
RESTRICT Age
```

Each RESTRICT statement removes the effect of the previous one and the last one leaves Age unrestricted. This is important as we may want to use Age later and operate on all its values.

The three histograms produced by the above statements would not necessarily be easy to compare, because the groups of ages chosen in each statement need not correspond. Comparability can be ensured by specifying the age groups in advance. The complete program and its output are then as shown below:

```
1   FACTOR[LABELS=!T(A,B,C,D,E,F,G,H,Z)]Party
2   OPEN'SURVEY.DAT';CHANNEL=2
3   READ[CHANNEL=2;LAYOUT=fixedfield;SKIP=*;SETNVALUES=yes]\
4     Age,Income,Party;FIELDWIDTH=2,5,1;SKIP=23,0,12;\
5     FREPRESENTATION=labels
```

Identifier	Minimum	Mean	Maximum	Values	Missing
Age	18.00	43.74	95.00	1723	27
Income	0	10833	41350	1723	218

```
6   RESTRICT Age; Party .EQ. 1
7   HISTOGRAM[LIMITS=!(20,25...65)]Age
```

Histogram of Age

```
   - 20    29  ***************
20 - 25    50  *************************
25 - 30    56  **************************
```

```
30 – 35      59   ****************************
35 – 40      66   *********************************
40 – 45     101   ****************************************************
45 – 50      72   ************************************
50 – 55      63   ******************************
55 – 60      72   ************************************
60 – 65      60   *****************************
65 –         94   ***********************************************
```

Scale: 1 asterisk represents 2 units.

```
 8   RESTRICT Age; Party .EQ. 2
 9   HISTOGRAM[LIMITS=!(20,25...65)]Age
```

Histogram of Age

```
  – 20      33   ****************
20 – 25      77   ****************************************
25 – 30      56   **************************
30 – 35      60   *****************************
35 – 40      35   *****************
40 – 45      30   ***************
45 – 50      23   ************
50 – 55      24   ************
55 – 60      21   ***********
60 – 65      32   ****************
65 –         39   *******************
```

Scale: 1 asterisk represents 2 units.

```
10   RESTRICT Age; Party .EQ. 3
11   HISTOGRAM[LIMITS=!(20,25...65)]Age
```

Histogram of Age

```
  – 20      10   *********
20 – 25      29   **************************
25 – 30      23   *********************
30 – 35      31   ****************************
35 – 40      26   ************************
40 – 45      39   *************************************
45 – 50      34   **********************************
50 – 55      38   *************************************
55 – 60      33   ********************************
60 – 65      16   ***************
65 –         49   ***********************************************
```

Scale: 1 asterisk represents 1 unit.

Notice that Genstat has used a reduced scale for the first two histograms to fit them on the page. To make the scale the same for all the histograms, set the option SCALE. For example, to get one asterisk for two units, include the setting SCALE=2 in each HISTOGRAM statement:

```
HISTOGRAM [LIMITS=!(20,25...65); SCALE=2] Age; GROUPS=LIMIT
```

8.3 Repeating statements

8.3.1 Loops

As mentioned above, the statements that produce the three histograms are repetitive, and they would be even more so if the data were illustrated for all nine parties (including the ninth, apolitical or secretive 'party'). Since Genstat programs are written in a language, rather than consisting of individual instructions to be executed one after the other, there is no problem in avoiding this long-windedness. The statements FOR and ENDFOR are provided to allow a sequence of statements to be executed several times over, changing individual items in the statements at each pass. The only item that needs to be changed in the three pairs of RESTRICT and HISTOGRAM statements above is the level number of the party being considered. So the RESTRICT and HISTOGRAM statements in the program in the last section can be replaced by:

```
FOR Level=1,2,3
    RESTRICT Age; Party .EQ. Level
    HISTOGRAM [LIMITS=!(20,25...65)] Age
ENDFOR
```

These statements are first executed with the value 1 substituted for the *dummy identifier* Level in the RESTRICT statement. When the ENDFOR statement is reached, execution returns to the FOR statement, this time substituting the value 2 for Level. Thus the statements in the *FOR loop* are executed repeatedly until the values in the list in the FOR statement are exhausted. The indentation is not necessary for the success of these statements, but it helps to make the structure of the program clear.

It is important to note that the identifier Level is not the identifier of a scalar or even a variate structure and so must not be declared as such. In fact it is a *dummy* structure, which stores the value it is currently pointing to — either 1, 2, or 3 in this example. But the value may be another identifier instead of a number. This is illustrated in the following statements to draw histograms of the two separate variables, age and income, for the first party's supporters:

```
FOR V=Age,Income
    RESTRICT V; Party .EQ. 1
    HISTOGRAM V
ENDFOR
```

The dummy identifier V now points in turn at the two variates Age and Income, to produce a histogram for each.

8.3.2 Nested loops

In order to produce the two histograms (age and income) for each party, two FOR loops must be *nested*, one inside the other:

```
FOR V=Age,Income
    FOR Level=1 ... 9
        RESTRICT V; Party .EQ. Level
        HISTOGRAM [LIMITS=!(20,25...65)] V
    ENDFOR
ENDFOR
```

During each pass through the outer loop Genstat will pass through the inner loop nine times and thus will examine all combinations of substitutions of V and Level.

8.3.3 Parallel loops

The histograms for income produced by the above statements would not be very informative, because the group limits are 20 up to 65 for both age and income! Clearly a separate variate of limits is needed for each variate. Another dummy identifier can be used to specify which of these variates of limits is to be used in each pass, and this dummy follows a semicolon separator (;) in the first FOR statement:

```
FOR V=Age,Income; Limit=!(20,25...65),!(3000,3500...12000)
    FOR Level=1...9
        RESTRICT V; Party .EQ. Level
        HISTOGRAM [LIMITS=Limit] V
    ENDFOR
ENDFOR
```

The first FOR statement can be thought of as specifying two loops to run in parallel and not nested one inside the other. Thus Genstat will not examine all combinations of V and Limit, as it does with V and Level; instead, Age and the unnamed variate !(20,25...65) are substituted for V and Limit respectively in the first pass, and Income and !(3000,3500...12000) are substituted in the second pass.

We do not show the output from these statements since it would take up several pages of this book. Eighteen histograms have been requested with a very few statements and this illustrates the convenience of the looping statements for repetitive tasks. But it would be well to think a little more before using these statements in practice. Many of the histograms produced may be practically useless since it is likely that some of the parties have very little support. It is not at all uncommon for a 'fringe' candidate to poll only 0.1 per cent in a political election and so we would expect to have interviewed only about two of this candidates's supporters in a random sample of 1723 people. A histogram of the ages of two people is just a waste of paper!

8.3.4 Avoiding statements in some circumstances

To avoid unnecessary executions of the HISTOGRAM statement above, Genstat must be told to ignore it when there are not enough people in a subset of the sample. The size of the subset is easy to extract:

```
CALCULATE Size = NVALUES(V)
```

The function NVALUES returns the number of values in a structure, taking account of the restriction in force, which defines the subset. The result is a scalar which can now be used to side-step the HISTOGRAM statement — we shall tell Genstat not to draw a histogram unless there are at least 20 people involved:

```
FOR V=Age,Income; Limit=!(20,24...65),!(3000,3500,12000)
    FOR Level=1...9
        RESTRICT V; Party .EQ. Level
        CALCULATE Size = NVALUES(V)
        IF Size .GE. 20
            HISTOGRAM [LIMITS=Limit] V
        ENDIF
    ENDFOR
ENDFOR
```

The HISTOGRAM statement is now executed only if the condition in the IF statement is met; that is, the value of Size is greater than or equal to 20. Otherwise

Genstat will move on to the ENDIF statement. (Note that there must be no space in this directive name: END IF is not valid.) Two further statements can be added to provide a warning when the condition is not met:

```
IF NVALUES(V) .GE. 20
    HISTOGRAM [LIMITS=Limit] V
ELSE
    PRINT 'Not enough data',Level
ENDIF
```

The PRINT statement is executed only if the condition is not met: otherwise Genstat skips from ELSE to the ENDIF statement. Notice that the CALCULATE statement has been dispensed with: the expression in an IF statement may contain functions in the same way as the expression in a CALCULATE statement.

8.4 Taking the data as they come: writing general programs

8.4.1 Defining the length of structures from the data

One of the most useful general features of the Genstat language is the facility to write general programs or series of statements; they can be used again and again with a variety of sets of data. Indeed, such series of statements can be formed into *procedures*, and stored permanently in the computer in the same way as numerical information and retrieved whenever required (see *Genstat 5: a second course*, or the *Genstat 5 reference manual* for more details).

We shall illustrate the writing of general programs by returning again to the simple program developed in Chapter 1. We shall recast it so it could be used to analyse a general set of data for the problem. To save leafing back to that chapter, here is a copy of the program, suitably amended to take advantage of the various features introduced in the intervening chapters.

```
UNITS [NVALUES=10]
READ Width,Height,Roomtemp
(data) :
CALCULATE Area = Width * Height
SCALAR Airtemp,Uchange; VALUE=5.7,2.0
CALCULATE Cashsave = (Roomtemp-Airtemp)*Area*Uchange*18.4*0.0051
PRINT Area,Cashsave; DECIMALS=3,2
STOP
```

The first step towards generalizing this program is to take out the data. Genstat is instructed to read them from a secondary file by opening the data file and putting a CHANNEL option in the READ statement:

```
OPEN 'WINDOW.DAT'; CHANNEL=2
READ [CHANNEL=2] Width,Height,Roomtemp
```

The program should now need no further modification for use with the data about 10 windows in any house, so long as the data are stored in a file called WINDOW.DAT.

Clearly not all houses have exactly 10 windows, so the program must allow for any number. It should not be difficult to ensure that the necessary data for each house are prepared in free format and terminated by a colon. So the option SETNVALUES=yes, introduced in Section 8.2.2, can be used to set the number of values of the variates Width, Height and Roomtemp instead of using a UNITS statement:

```
READ [CHANNEL=2; SETNVALUES=yes] Width,Height,Roomtemp
```

The number of values of the variates Area and Cashsave will be defined automatically by CALCULATE, as explained in Chapter 5 (Section 5.2.1).

8.4.2 Storing identifiers in pointer structures

The last part of the program uses some constants describing the house under investigation. The length of the heating season, the average air temperature outside the house and the cost of heat will differ from house to house. But the same value, 2.0, can probably be assumed for the change in conductivity due to double-glazing in any house. Thus three further numbers will be required in the data file. They can be stored in scalars:

```
SCALAR Airtemp,Season,Cost
READ [CHANNEL=2] Airtemp,Season,Cost
CALCULATE Cashsave = (Roomtemp-Airtemp)*Area*2*Season*Cost
```

The program can be shortened by making use of a further shorthand technique at this point:

```
POINTER [VALUES=Airtemp,Season,Cost] Constant
SCALAR Constant[]
READ Constant[]
```

The POINTER declaration allows a single identifier, here Constant, to be used in place of a list of identifiers that is needed several times. Pointers were mentioned in Chapter 5 (Section 5.2.3), when suffixes were introduced. The POINTER declaration above has the effect that the suffixed identifier Constant[1] refers to the structure Airtemp; similarly Constant[2] and Constant[3] refer to Season and Cost. The *null suffix* [] is a concise way of representing all the identifiers contained in a pointer; here, Constant[] is the same as Constant[1...3].

The program now consists of the following statements:

```
OPEN 'WINDOW.DAT'; CHANNEL=2
READ [CHANNEL=2; SETNVALUES=yes] Width,Height,Roomtemp
POINTER [VALUES=Airtemp,Season,Cost] Constant
SCALAR Constant[]
READ [CHANNEL=2] Constant[]
CALCULATE Area = Width * Height
& Cashsave = (Roomtemp-Airtemp)*Area*2*Season*Cost
PRINT Area,Cashsave; DECIMALS=3,2
STOP
```

This program can be used for any set of data that is prepared in the following form:

(widths, heights and room temperatures
 ordered in parallel, presented in free format)
:

(air temperature) (season length) (cost of heat)
:

Notice that a colon is given after the values that are to be read into the scalar structures, in the same way as a colon is given after the values to be read into variates.

8.5 Summary

Chapter 8 introduces more complicated methods of programming with the Genstat language.

When data are not recorded in free format the READ statement must include settings of the options LAYOUT and SKIP, indicating how the input records are organized, and of the parameters FIELDWIDTH and SKIP specifying where the data values are to be found on each input record.

The END option can be used to avoid using the end-of-data marker (:), and the SETNVALUES option can be used to define the length of data structures from the number of data values.

The statement RESTRICT can be used to restrict attention to a subset of the data so that analyses or summaries can be produced for the subset.

Sections of program may be repeated, or avoided conditionally on some logical criterion, by using the following statements:

FOR marks the start of a loop which is to be repeated with dummy identifiers taking new values at each pass,

ENDFOR marks the end of a loop,

IF introduces a condition to be evaluated, and a series of statements that are to be executed if the condition is true,

ELSE introduces a series of statements to be executed if the condition is false,

ENDIF marks the end of conditional execution.

A list of identifiers can be replaced by the identifier of a pointer structure that contains the identifiers, together with a null suffix [].

8.6 Exercises

8(1) Create a file in your computer holding 600 numbers; do not put an end-of-data marker at the end of the file. For example, you could use Genstat to produce some pseudo-random numbers with the function URAND (give the command

HELP systemfunction,URAND

to find out about this function). Print the numbers without any labelling by an identifier using the option IPRINT=* in the PRINT statement.

Write a program to read the numbers into a variate from the data file you have set up. Find their mean and variance with the functions MEAN and VARIANCE (Chapter 5, Section 5.2.2). Then find separately the mean and variance for the first 100 numbers, the second 100 and so on. If the numbers are random, all the means and variances should be similar.

8(2) Record the data from Exercise 6(2) (in Chapter 6) with a fixed format. Use exactly four columns for rainfall and windspeed and five for temperature, and use only the first 13 columns of each record. Thus the first line of your data should be:

    5.71 4.497.30

Read the values for temperature and windspeed into two variates, ignoring the rainfall. Plot the average temperatures in February at all the sites and in both the years against the corresponding windspeeds, and similarly for July. Put informative titles on the axes of each graph. Though there are only two graphs to draw, use the FOR statement in this exercise.

8(3) Read the rainfall values from the data recorded as in Exercise 8(2). Find the mean rainfall for each county within each month in each year. Print the means one under another, excluding any that are less than 1 mm. To do this you must use RESTRICT rather than setting up a table, and you need to know how to restrict to levels of several factors at the same time. If A and B are factors and V is a variate you can restrict to level 1 of A and level 3 of B by

```
RESTRICT V; A.EQ.1 .AND. B.EQ.3
```

(There is a similar logical operator called .OR.)

Alongside the means print an index of month, year, and county; print just the numbers 1 or 2 to indicate first or second year, and so on. Print a title above the results to give column headings for the indices, and use the option SQUASH=yes in the PRINT statement, to suppress blank lines in the output.

APPENDIX Solutions to the exercises

CHAPTER 1

Exercise 1(1)

```
VARIATE [NVALUES=12] Sowdate,Harvdate,Rain,Sun
READ Sowdate,Harvdate,Rain,Sun
  90   218   11.8   587
  96   239   12.6   604
  87   220   11.3   431
 104   247   10.0   522
  89   229    2.5   724
  91   230   18.7   398
  86   227    6.5   473
 110   252   11.1   465
 107   246    4.3   591
  83   218   13.6   421
  99   254   30.8   266
  88   231    8.9   672:
VARIATE [NVALUES=12] Days,Averain,Avesun
CALCULATE Days = Harvdate—Sowdate
CALCULATE Averain = Rain*2.54/Days
CALCULATE Avesun = Sun/Days
PRINT Averain
PRINT Avesun
PRINT Averain,Avesun; DECIMALS=3,2
STOP
```

Exercise 1(2)

```
VARIATE [VALUES=1,2,3,5,7,11,13,17,19] Radius
VARIATE [NVALUES=9] Area
CALCULATE Area = 3.142*(Radius**2)
PRINT Radius,Area; DECIMALS=0,2
STOP
```

There is no special symbol for π in Genstat. If you want to be exact, then use the arcsine function: 2*ARCSIN(1) (functions are introduced in Chapter 5). But statisticians may appreciate that 3 is accurate to within 5 per cent!

Exercise 1(3)

```
VARIATE [NVALUES=10] Width,Height,Roomtemp,Cashsave
READ Width,Height,Roomtemp
0.39   0.55   17.1
1.05   1.18   17.1
2.40   1.96   16.6
2.06   1.26   16.6
0.48   0.90   14.5
0.56   0.96   14.5
1.06   0.98   16.2
1.54   0.96   14.5
1.04   0.96   14.5
2.02   0.92   15.0:
CALCULATE Cashsave = (Roomtemp-5.7)*Width*Height*2*18.4*0.0051
PRINT Cashsave
STOP
```

CHAPTER 2

Exercise 2(1)

Say the file containing the data for rainfall and sunshine is called WEATHER.DAT.

```
OPEN 'WEATHER.DAT'; CHANNEL=2
VARIATE [NVALUES=12] Sowdate,Harvdate,Rain,Sun
READ [CHANNEL=2] Sowdate,Harvdate,Rain,Sun
CALCULATE Rain = Rain*2.54
CALCULATE Sun = Sun/24
PRINT Rain,Sun
STOP
```

If the file containing the program is called EX21.GEN, then the following command (or something like it in the language of your operating system) will produce the results in file EX21.OUT:

```
GENSTAT EX21.GEN,EX21.OUT
```

Exercise 2(2)

```
VARIATE [NVALUES=10] Number,Square,Cube
READ Number
1 2 3 4 5 6 7 8 9 10:
CALCULATE Square = Number**2
CALCULATE Cube = Square*Number
PRINT Number,Square,Cube; DECIMALS=0
STOP
```

Exercise 2(3)

```
OPEN 'EX23.CPY'; CHANNEL=2; FILETYPE=output
COPY 2
VARIATE [NVALUES=10] Number,Square,Cube
READ Number
1 2 3 4 5 6 7 8 9 10:
CALCULATE Square = Number**2
CALCULATE Cube = Square*Number
OPEN 'EX23.RES'; CHANNEL=3; FILETYPE=output
PRINT [CHANNEL=3] Number,Square,Cube; DECIMALS=0
STOP
```

CHAPTER 3

Exercise 3(1)

```
VARIATE [NVALUES=40] Height
READ Height
0.55    1.26    0.53    0.26    1.23    1.15    0.31    1.22    1.13    0.39
1.10    1.06    1.10    0.43    1.18    0.81    0.99    1.25    0.18    1.13
1.09    1.24    1.35    1.14    1.29    1.10    1.25    1.14    1.14    0.30
1.22    0.25    0.15    1.15    1.17    1.45    1.20    1.33    1.16    1.11:
HISTOGRAM Height
STOP
```

Exercise 3(2)

```
VARIATE [NVALUES=15] Shoot,Motivate,Gsr
READ Shoot,Motivate,Gsr
```

```
25   8   0.82   32   7   1.08   62   6   0.71   40   1   0.28   25   1   0.33
52   7   0.89   56   6   0.84   55   3   0.41   60   2   0.49   47   2   0.42
12   1   0.17   89   4   0.44   15   7   1.06   83   6   0.71   88   5   0.46:
TEXT Ts; VALUE='Shooting score'
GRAPH [YTITLE=Ts; XTITLE='Motivation'; YLOWER=0; YUPPER=100]\
    Y=Shoot;  X=Motivate
GRAPH [YTITLE=Ts; XTITLE='Gsr reading'; YLOWER=0; YUPPER=100]\
    Y=Shoot;  X=Gsr
STOP
```

Exercise 3(3)

```
VARIATE [NVALUES=12] Month,Rate,Temp
READ  Month,Rate,Temp
1   561   -1    2   522    3    3   466    6    4   413    8
5   317   13    6   236   16    7   245   16    8   312   13
9   305   14   10   367   10   11   521    2   12   562    0:
TEXT Tm,Tr,Tt; VALUES='Months','Rate / megawatts',\
    'Temperature / deg C'
GRAPH [YTITLE=Tr; XTITLE=Tm; YLOWER=0; XLOWER=0] Y=Rate;\
    X=Month;  METHOD=line
GRAPH [YTITLE=Tt; XTITLE=Tm; XLOWER=0] Y=Temp; X=Month;\
    METHOD=line
CALCULATE Rate = Rate*0.1
TEXT Tn; VALUES='Temperature / deg C and Rate / megawatts*0.1'
GRAPH [YTITLE=Tn; XTITLE=Tm; XLOWER=0] Y=Temp,Rate,Temp,Rate;\
    X=Month;  METHOD=line,line,point,point;\
    SYMBOL='.','.','T','E'
STOP
```

CHAPTER 4

Exercise 4(1)

```
VARIATE [NVALUES=16] Reading,Count
READ  Reading,Count
0.37    8.2   0.64   12.1   0.84
15.8    0.59  10.6    0.77  14.2   0.7118.2
0.48    7.3   0.78   16.1   1.02   16.8
0.62   13.3   0.93   15.0   0.91   19.1
```

```
0.74    11.4    0.81    16.9    0.94    23.4
0.71    12.9:
MODEL Count
FIT Reading
RKEEP FITTEDVALUES=Fitted
GRAPH Fitted,Count; X=Reading; METHOD=line,point
STOP
```

The regression coefficient of the reading is 19.3 with standard error 3.7. The constant is very small, so it may be reasonable to fit a regression through the origin. Also, it seems from the graph that the variance of the residuals is not constant; one solution to this problem would be to weight each count by the inverse of the reading, or of the reading squared. This is done as follows:

```
CALCULATE W = 1/(Reading**2)
MODEL [WEIGHT=W] Count
FIT [CONSTANT=omit] Reading
```

Exercise 4(2)

```
VARIATE [NVALUES=10] Time,Wtdiff
READ  Time,Wtdiff
0.0     0.21    0.5    —1.46    1.0    —3.04    1.5    —3.21    2.0    —5.04
2.5    —5.37    3.0    —6.03    3.5    —7.21    4.0    —7.46    4.5    —7.96:
CALCULATE Time2 = Time**2
MODEL Wtdiff
TERMS Time,Time2
FIT Time,Time2
RKEEP FITTEDVALUES=Fit2; RESIDUALS=Res2
GRAPH Res2; Fit2
GRAPH Res2; Time
DROP Time2
RKEEP FITTEDVALUES=Fit; RESIDUALS=Res
GRAPH Res; Fit
GRAPH Res; Time
STOP
```

Exercise 4(3)

```
VARIATE [NVALUES=15] Cand,Total,Comp,Prev
READ  Cand,Total,Comp,Prev
```

1	476	111	68	2	457	92	46	3	540	90	46
4	551	107	59	5	575	98	50	6	698	150	66
7	545	118	54	8	574	110	51	9	645	117	59
10	556	94	97	11	634	130	57	12	637	118	51
13	390	91	44	14	562	118	61	15	560	109	66:

```
MODEL Total
TERMS Comp,Prev
FIT Comp
ADD [PRINT=model,summary,estimates,fitted] Prev
STOP
```

CHAPTER 5

Exercise 5(1)

```
UNITS [NVALUES=27]
VARIATE X,T; VALUES=!(1...27),!(21,25...125)
READ Y
   0    2    4    7    8   10   12   15   16   19   21   24   25   28
  31   32   35   38   40   42   44   47   49   51   54   57   59:
CALCULATE Logy = LOG(0.35+Y)
& X2 = (X—MEAN(X))**2
MODEL Logy
TERMS X,X2
FIT X
RKEEP RESIDUALS=R
ADD X2
RKEEP RESIDUALS=S
GRAPH [YTITLE='Residuals'; XTITLE='TIME'] R; T
& S; T
STOP
```

The shortest possible version of this program is given below (note that STOP is not actually needed). It is much harder to read than the program above, so we suggest you do not model your future programs on this version!

```
VARI X, T, Y;!(1...27), !(21, 25...125), !(0, 2, 4, 7, 8, 10, 12, 15, 16, 19,\
    21,24,25,28,31,32,35,38,40,42,44,47,49,51,54,57,59)
CALC Logy=LOG(.35+Y)&X2=(X—MEAN(X))**2:MODE Logy:TERM X,X2:FIT X
RKEE;R:ADD X2:RKEE;S:GRAP[;;'Residuals';'TIME']R;T&S;T
```

Exercise 5(2)

SX 49 and VA 13: Values of a variate that are assigned in the VALUES parameter must be combined with the !() notation. Genstat matches all parameter lists with the first, so Time has been given the single value 0.

SX 6: The setting of SERIAL must be 'no' or 'yes' (or n,y,ye).

SX 10: Both faults occur because Genstat has not accepted the READ statement and so is looking for statements rather than data values.

SX 13: There should be two opening round brackets before 1.25.

SX 12: The string must be quoted since it contains a space and brackets; it could also be enclosed in !T(), though this is not necessary when a text has a single quoted string as a value.

SX 2: The previous statement failed, so the ampersand is not valid.

SX 5: The second option should be named XTITLE.

The second statement has an extra fault: the progression 0...8 contains nine values, not eight. The seventh statement will also be faulted again once the string is quoted: the identifier Time has been used already for a variate, and so cannot be redefined as a text. The same is true of Conc in the eighth statement.

Exercise 5(3)

```
VARIATE [NVALUES=10] Week[1...8]
READ [SERIAL=yes] Week[1...8]
   4   2   0   5   1   0   1   0   0   0:
   8   0   0   9   1   0   3   0   1   0:
  12   1   0  12   2   2   3   0   4   0:
  19   3   0  26   4   1   2   0   3   1:
  24   5   0  21   9   3   4   3   2   0:
  28   0   0  15  13   2   6  11   0   1:
  31   2   0   5   4   0   7  25   3   0:
  35   1   0   1   1   1   5  43   0   0:
CALCULATE Week[2...8] = Week[1...7]+Week[2...8]
CALCULATE Week[1...8] = Week[1...8]*100/Week[8]
PRINT Week[1...8]
VARIATE [NVALUES=8] S[1...10]
READ S[1...10]
   4   2   0   5   1   0   1   0   0   0
   8   0   0   9   1   0   3   0   1   0
  12   1   0  12   2   2   3   0   4   0
  19   3   0  26   4   1   2   0   3   1
  24   5   0  21   9   3   4   3   2   0
```

```
28   0   0   15  13   2   6   11   0   1
31   2   0    5   4   0   7   25   3   0
35   1   0    1   1   1   5   43   0   0:
CALCULATE Species[1...10] = CUMULATE(S[1...10])*100\
    / SUM(S[1...10]) PRINT Species[1...10]
STOP
```

The first CALCULATE statement could be written as seven separate statements:

```
CALCULATE Week[2] = Week[1]+Week[2]
&          Week[3] = Week[2]+Week[3] ...
```

but it is better to put them together. Genstat will do the calculations one at a time anyway, so that, for example, Week[2] is worked out before the calculation for Week[3] uses it.

CHAPTER 6

Exercise 6(1)

```
UNITS [NVALUES=48]
FACTOR [LEVELS=4; VALUES=12(1...4)] Adhesive
VARIATE [VALUES=100,200,300] psi; DECIMALS=0
FACTOR [LEVELS=psi; VALUES=(100,200,300)16] Pressure
READ Strength
14   14   10   14   10   12   14   19   13   17   15   10   11   16   19   15   15   10
17   11   14   30   10    8   15   16   18   23   26   16   24   15    6   15   18   22
 3   20   23    9   18   12    6   21   17    9   10   13       :
TABULATE [CLASSIFICATION=Pressure,Adhesive; PRINT=means]\
    Strength; MEANS=Meanstr
MARGIN Meanstr; METHOD=means
PRINT Meanstr
STOP
```

Exercise 6(2)

```
UNITS [NVALUES=16]
FACTOR [LABELS=!T(Ayrshire,Cornwall); VALUES=8(1,2)] Site
& [LABELS=!T(February,July); VALUES=2(1,2)4] Month
FACTOR [LEVELS=!(1977,1978); VALUES=4(1977,1978)2] Year;\
    DECIMALS=0
```

```
READ  Rainfall,Temp,Windsp
5.71     4.49     7.30     2.20     3.84     7.43     0.50    17.59     4.49
1.97    16.94     4.63     2.51     4.49     5.14     0.00    -0.84     2.67
2.99    11.47     7.81     0.00    13.87     4.57     5.66     7.69     4.41
4.93     7.86     3.00     0.44    17.26     2.37     5.44    15.76     3.17
3.44     7.47     5.46     0.29     0.53     4.80     1.70    12.56     5.74
0.79    14.29     2.86:
TABLE [CLASSIFICATION=Year,Month,Site]\
    Meanrain,Meantemp,Meanwind
TABULATE Rainfall,Temp,Windsp; MEANS=Meanrain,Meantemp,Meanwind
PRINT Meanrain,Meantemp,Meanwind; DECIMALS=2
```

Exercise 6(3)

```
UNITS [NVALUES=51]
FACTOR [LABELS=!T(M,A)] Gearbox
FACTOR [LEVELS=!(1,1.3); VALUES=21(1),30(1.3)] Capacity;\
    DECIMALS=1
FACTOR [LABELS=!T(Urban,'90km/hr','120km/hr');\
    VALUES=(1,2,3)17] Speed
READ Gearbox,Fuel; FREPRESENTATION=labels
M 7.6    M 5.5    M 7.5    M 7.4    M 5.3    M 7.3    M 6.8    M 4.8    M 6.8
M 7.7    M 5.8    M 8.5    A 7.0    A 7.3    A *      M 7.5    M 5.9    M 8.6
A 7.6    A 7.8    A *
M 8.9    M 6.3    M 8.3    A 8.1    A 6.9    A 9.2    M 8.6    M 5.5    M 7.5
M 8.9    M 6.1    M 8.4    A 9.0    A 6.9    A 9.4    M 9.5    M 6.5    M 9.4
A 9.7    A 7.2    A 10.6   M 9.5    M 6.4    M 9.0    A 9.8    A 6.9    A 9.8
M 9.8    M 6.0    M 8.3:
TABULATE [PRINT=means,totals,nobservations;\
    CLASSIFICATION=Speed,Capacity; MARGINS=yes] Fuel
TABULATE [CLASSIFICATION=Capacity,Speed,Gearbox; MARGINS=yes]\
    Fuel; MEANS=Meanfuel
PRINT Meanfuel; DECIMALS=1
TABLE [CLASSIFICATION=Speed; MARGINS=yes] Meanmarg
CALCULATE Meanmarg = Meanfuel
& %Mean = 100*Meanfuel/Meanmarg
PRINT %Mean; DECIMALS=1
```

CHAPTER 7

Exercise 7(1)

```
UNITS [NVALUES=29]
FACTOR [LEVELS=4; VALUES=6(1...4),1,2,4,2,4] Diet
READ Weight
3.42    3.17    3.34    3.64
3.96    3.63    3.72    3.93
3.87    3.38    3.81    3.77
4.19    3.47    3.66    4.18
3.58    3.39    3.55    4.21
3.76    3.41    3.51    3.88
3.84    3.55            3.96
        3.44            3.91:
TREATMENTS Diet
ANOVA Weight
STOP
```

Exercise 7(2)

```
UNITS [NVALUES=16]
FACTOR [LEVELS=4; VALUES=(1...4)4] Rabbit
& [LEVELS=!(23,25,26,27); VALUES=4(23,25,26,27)] Date;\
    DECIMALS=0
FACTOR [LABELS=!T(A,B,C,D)] Dose
READ Dose,Response; FREPRESENTATION=labels
B 24    C 46    D 34    A 48
D 33    A 58    B 57    C 60
A 57    D 26    C 60    B 45
C 46    B 34    A 61    D 47:
BLOCKS Date+Rabbit
TREATMENTS Dose
ANOVA Response
STOP
```

Exercise 7(3)

```
UNITS [NVALUES=48]
FACTOR [LEVELS=3; VALUES=16(1...3)] Rep
& [LEVELS=8; VALUES=((1...4)2,(5...8)2)3] Fldplot
```

```
FACTOR [LABELS=!T(V,W); VALUES=8(1,2)3] Weedcont
 & [LABELS=!T(M,N); VALUES=4(1,2)6] Estmeth
 & [LABELS=!T(P,Q,R,S); VALUES=(1...4)12] Cultseq
READ Yield
4.73    4.65    8.70    10.78    0.61    6.31    3.45     8.49
4.36    6.02    9.29    13.13    5.65    9.74    7.63    12.00
3.23    6.29    3.69     6.95    1.66    4.41    3.48     5.70
2.10    5.92    9.42    10.09    3.54    7.38    7.72     9.62
3.69    6.12    6.41     8.91    4.84    0.78    7.03     5.96
6.99    8.33    8.52    11.21    4.04    8.64    8.10     7.88 :
BLOCKS Rep / Fldplot
TREATMENTS Weedcont * Cultseq * Estmeth
ANOVA Yield
STOP
```

CHAPTER 8

Exercise 8(1)

The file of numbers can be created by the following program:

```
CALCULATE X = URAND(15863; 600)
OPEN 'EX81.DAT'; CHANNEL=4; FILETYPE=output
PRINT [CHANNEL=4; IPRINT=*] X
CLOSE 4; FILETYPE=output
STOP
```

The following program reads from this file and summarizes the values:

```
VARIATE [NVALUES=600] X
OPEN 'EX81.DAT'; CHANNEL=3
READ [CHANNEL=3; END=*] X
CALCULATE Mean600 = MEAN(X)
 & Var600 = VARIANCE(X)
PRINT Mean600,Var600
FACTOR [LEVELS=6; VALUES=100(1...6)] Group
FOR Level=1...6
    RESTRICT X; Group==Level
    CALCULATE Mean100 = MEAN(X)
     & Var100 = VARIANCE(X)
```

```
        PRINT Mean100,Var100
ENDFOR
STOP
```

Exercise 8(2)

```
UNITS [NVALUES=16]
FACTOR [LEVELS=2; VALUES=2(1,2)4] Month
READ [LAYOUT=fixedfield; SKIP=*] Temp,Windsp;\
    FIELDWIDTH=5,4; SKIP=4,0
5.71  4.497.30
2.20  3.847.43
0.5017.594.49
1.9716.944.63
2.51  4.495.14
0.00-0.842.67
2.9911.477.81
0.0013.874.57
5.66  7.694.41
4.93  7.863.00
0.4417.262.37
5.4415.763.17
3.44  7.475.46
0.29  0.534.80
1.7012.565.74
0.7914.292.86:
FOR Level=1,2; Title='Windspeed in February',\
    'Windspeed in July'
    RESTRICT Temp,Windsp; Month==Level
    GRAPH [YTITLE='Average temperature'; XTITLE=Title] Temp;\
        Windsp
ENDFOR
STOP
```

Exercise 8(3)

```
UNITS [NVALUES=16]
FACTOR [LEVELS=2] Site,Month,Year;\
    VALUES=!(8(1,2)),!(2(1,2)4),!(4(1,2)2)
READ [LAYOUT=fixedfield; SKIP=*] Rainfall; FIELDWIDTH=4
5.71  4.497.30
```

```
2.20 3.847.43
0.5017.594.49
1.9716.944.63
2.51 4.495.14
0.00-0.842.67
2.9911.477.81
0.0013.874.57
5.66 7.694.41
4.93 7.863.00
0.4417.262.37
5.4415.763.17
3.44 7.475.46
0.29 0.534.80
1.7012.565.74
0.7914.292.86:
PRINT ' Year Month Site Rainfall'
FOR Y=1,2
   FOR M=1,2
      FOR C=1,2
         RESTRICT Rainfall;Year==Y .AND. Month==M .AND. Site==C
         CALCULATE Mrain = MEAN(Rainfall)
         IF Mrain>=1
           PRINT [IPRINT=*; SQUASH=yes] Y,M,C,Mrain;\
              FIELDWIDTH=3(6),10; DECIMALS=3(0),2
         ENDIF
      ENDFOR
   ENDFOR
ENDFOR
STOP
```

Index

This index contains entries for all items in the Genstat language introduced in this book, together with references to English words and phrases. Entries have been combined where a Genstat item is also an English word; so, for example, references for calculation are found under CALCULATE. Option and parameter names are given only under the entries for each directive. No references have been made to the summaries nor to the content of examples or exercises except where new information about Genstat is also presented.